SNOW'S KITCHEN

A NOVELLA AND COOKBOOK

AMY M. LE

SNOW'S KITCHEN

Copyright © 2020 by Amy M. Le

First edition December 2020

Jacket design by Virginia McKevitt

Manufactured in the United States of America

ISBN: 978-1-7351194-3-4 (ebook)
ISBN: 978-1-7351194-4-1 (paperback)
ISBN: 978-1-7351194-5-8 (hardback)

DEDICATION

This book is dedicated to anyone who has ever felt adrift in life. May you find your tribe and hang your hat where friends, family, and food bond you together. Above all else, never give up on yourself even when others have.

PRAISE FOR SNOW'S KITCHEN

"A delicious read!"
"Had my heart pounding!"
"So hard to read, but so good!"
"My eyes were leaking...really good!"
"Amy's cooking as well as her writing is legit."
"I live in suspense from one chapter to the next!"
"This book has so much more emotion than the previous ones!"
—Beta Readers of "Snow's Kitchen: A Novella and Cookbook"

"Author Amy Le has written a heartrending coming of age story in Snow's Kitchen. We follow Dolly, a young Vietnamese refugee, on a journey to discover her identity. She's caught between two cultures as she tries to live up to the expectations of her Vietnamese mom and stepdad while yearning for the independence America has promised. No matter the trials or struggles, Dolly and her mom, Snow, reconnect in the kitchen over their shared love of food. I enjoyed this highly engaging book and am looking forward to trying the recipes from Snow's Kitchen."
—Staci Mauney, Editor, Prestige Prose

"Snow's Kitchen is an amazing combination between a book and a cookbook. This installment is told from Dolly's view of life. It is both intriguing and inspiring. While reading Dolly's story, you can feel the emotions of all the characters. Dolly expresses her love and admiration for her mother with so much passion you can feel love. You can also feel her pain, hate, and sometimes the darkness she faced. Dolly reels you in and keeps you engaged with the struggles and adversities she had to encounter during her formative years. And these recipes! I can't wait to try them out! By far one of the best novellas I have ever read. One I am proud to display in my library and will read again and again."
—Tabitha Salom, Beta Reader

Left to right: Derrick Adkins, Kristina Williams, Sarah Alpar

"I'm always more than happy to be Amy's guinea pig. She never disappoints! Even her experiments are tasty."
—Derrick "A-Game" Adkins, MMA Coach out of American Elite

"Amy is a true artist in the kitchen. Not only does her food look like a masterpiece it tastes like one as well!"
—Kristina "Warhorse" Williams, Professional MMA Fighter

"You can taste and smell what you're reading! Beautifully described and written."
—Sarah "Too Sweet" Alpar, UFC Fighter, Bantamweight

ACKNOWLEDGMENTS

I wrote this novella in one month and it was in large part due to my NaNoWriMo buddies, Barbara Shepherd and Kyle Peltier. Thank you for rooting me on! Thank you to my husband, Joe, for being the most patient photographer and partner in life. To my son, Preston, thanks for your candid feedback. You both offered encouragement with brutal honesty and enthusiastic gluttony. To my taste testers, thank you for lending your taste buds to scientific experiments. I'm happy you survived my cooking to endorse this book! To my critique team, Ilene Birkwood, Tricia Corbett, Lori Kennedy, Diana LeBeau, Melissa Martin, and Tabitha Salom, your feedback was invaluable and helped me get this story out of my heart into the minds of the readers. Finally, to Staci Mauney, my editor at Prestige Prose, and Virginia McKevitt, my cover designer with Black Widow Books, you both are the best partners any author could ever want. Thank you for taking my books from good to great!

INTRODUCTION

In 2017, I embarked on a life-changing journey of self-discovery. After my mama, Snow, passed from cancer, I quit my corporate job and never looked back.

To honor the brave and incredible woman who raised me, I wrote my debut, historical fiction novel, *Snow in Vietnam,* to share with the world our family's story of survival after the fall of Saigon. The sequel, *Snow in Seattle,* was my women's fiction novel of the Vietnamese diaspora and detailed our immigrant story of rebuilding and thriving in a new country while grappling with trauma and PTSD.

Snow's Kitchen is the final book in the *Snow* trilogy and was written in one month during NaNoWriMo 2020. It is dedicated to all the drifters and gourmands out there. I wanted to honor my mother's love for food by sharing with you some of her recipes. I also included some of my favorite recipes that I created or enhanced over the years.

Snow was born in Tra Vinh, Vietnam in 1939. She was the youngest of seven children and after the Vietnam War ended, she left her country in search of freedom. Like hundreds of thousands of refugees, my mother feared persecution, faced starvation and lost everything.

It was not until 1980 after my mother resettled in America that she took an interest in cooking. With one foot in the past and one in the present, she straddled the cultures of East and West and bounced between dystopia and utopia. Her flair for food represented the fusion of two worlds.

The first half of this book is a novella written from Dolly's perspective. Follow along as she navigates her way through adolescence experiencing a spectrum of emotions from love and pain to determination and self-discovery.

In the second half, I share with you our family recipes. Some of the foods are traditional but prepared with modern methods, while some recipes were borrowed and turned into something unique. I welcome you to Snow's kitchen and hope the foods inspire you, excite you, and introduce you to new flavors.

For my fans who could not wait for this book, I challenge you to try some recipes. Post pictures of your oopsies and hurrays on social media with **#SnowsKitchen**.

Enjoy and blessings to you all!

Amy M. Le aka Dolly

Liz Nguyen aka Snow

SNOW'S KITCHEN
A NOVELLA

1. BOYS ARE STUPID (SUMMER 1988)

The first boy I ever kissed was named Dung. Let that marinate for a second. In Vietnamese, the name Dũng means heroic, but when you're a thirteen-year-old refugee boy living in Westminster, California, your name means shit, literally and figuratively. No way was I going to date a boy whose name translated to "poop."

In the summer of '88, I turned fourteen. My mom, Snow, and my stepdad, Binh, agreed to let me go to the carnival down the street. They gave me thirty dollars and a list of don'ts. Mom sent my cousin, Tree, to keep an eye on me, and Binh sent his son, Khoi, to spy on me. Unbeknownst to my parents, both Tree and Khoi each gave me ten dollars and told me to be home by ten.

Heroic-Poop and I were classmates at Johnson Middle School, where we had spent three months flirting from thirty feet away. Naturally, I fantasized about our first kiss. I used my last ride ticket on the Zipper and was determined to have that kiss.

"Dear God," I prayed, "may he be brave as his name implies and his kiss as explosive as fireworks. Oh, and please encourage him to change his name to something cool, like John Stamos or Rob Lowe."

Inside the steel carriage, I wondered how many times the padded cage had been wiped down over the years from all the vomit and sloppy wet kisses. Oh, if only the Zipper could talk. The fair attendant secured our straps and locked the gate. Dung and I held hands. We locked eyes. This was it.

While the world outside swirled in a blur, inside, we moved like two sloths finding our way to puckered lips. Then it happened. Our heads banged together from the G-force, and our lips skidded like two cars drifting around a bend. Saigon Drift.

I tasted wet, curdled chunks of pâté and bread. I screamed. Dung was mortified.

"I'm sorry," he said. "Christine, I'll buy you another shirt."

"You threw up on me," I yelled.

It took me months of flirting and two and a half minutes of being tossed around a metal crate to realize boys are stupid.

Dung was a turd after all.

I had moved from Seattle to San Jose the previous summer with my mom, Snow, and her fiancé, Binh. I was miserable. I didn't have my friends Nadirah, Marina, Jackie, Melissa, or Jen with me. I even missed knock-kneed Jason and stupid Hung, who threw a dead snake at me when we were in the second grade.

Right away my parents put me to work without pay. On the weekends, I went with Thu to the San Jose Flea Market where we had a booth and sold silk flower arrangements, ceramic vases, and ceramic elephants. During the week, Binh and Thu fired up the kilns to bake the clay molds. Mama and I hand-painting the elephants and tall vases. It was fun at first until it became a family business and making money was the priority. I dreaded the chore that it became.

My soon-to-be stepbrother, Khoi, understood my weary and lonely heart and surprised me with a gift.

"Tiên," Khoi said, "Linh and I have declared this Saturday 'Tiên Day.'"

Even though he broke my Vietnamese name Thủy-Tiên apart and shortened it to Tiên, I forgave him. I couldn't stay mad at charming, handsome, funny, and easygoing Khoi for long. He could have called me Richard, and I'd have been as happy as a soaring eagle. His girlfriend, Linh, was the perfect match for him. She was an aspiring model with gorgeous legs, sleek black hair, and heart-shaped lips. She was the kindest soul on Earth, and I wanted to be her.

"What do we do on Tien Day?" I asked.

"You'll see," he answered with a wink.

That Saturday Khoi excused me from flea market duty without consulting Thu. She threw a handful of paintbrushes at him and called him a lousy brother.

Khoi and Linh picked me up from the house and took me to a hair salon. Linh and I got our hair done while Khoi disappeared for an hour. He came back in time to see the drama unfold.

"Linh, why is she crying?" Khoi asked.

Linh panicked. "Christine, you look so cute!" She tried to cheer me up, but it didn't work.

I had asked the stylist for a Princess Diana cut, but the moment his scissors assaulted my long, wavy hair, my eyes burned and leaked. Tendrils and snippets of wet black locks fell to the tile floor as I mourned the loss of my hair. I sank into my chair to sulk.

I gave the stylist a sharp stare. "I look diseased." In my mind, I thought I would look like the Princess of Wales, but the face staring back at me was a dark, sickly wannabe with small black eyes and the wrong shaped face.

Khoi paid for my haircut and tipped the man generously to make up for my embarrassing reaction.

"Why are boys so stupid?" I asked Linh. "If a girl had cut my hair, she would have gotten it right."

"Hey, now." Khoi raised his hand. "Boy present here."

"You're not a boy," I said. "You're Khoi."

Linh burst into giggles and playfully pinched Khoi's cheeks. "Ah, you hear that? You're my boy Khoi. Princess Christine said so."

We had a good laugh, and all was forgiven. The next stop was lunch. We visited Lee's Sandwiches for *bánh mì* and coffee, and I told them I was getting a puppy. My mama had promised I could have any dog under twenty-five pounds.

"It's still Tien Day," I said. "What's next?"

We drove to San Francisco, but before heading to the wharf, Khoi and Linh dropped by their apartment to get their sunglasses. Inside their small, cute home, I detected a faint urine odor. Linh and Khoi didn't seem to notice. They disappeared into the bathroom together, which was odd, but I concluded their sunglasses must be in there.

"What in the world?" I heard Khoi exclaim.

"Oh my!" Linh yelled out.

I darted to the bathroom and squeezed in between them. I shrieked.

Her eyes were small, round charcoal bits. Her coat was short and fawn-colored. Her ears drooped, and her small tail wagged fast. On a snowy Seattle day, she could have cleared all the roads in our neighborhood with her tail. I scooped the Chihuahua into my arms and kissed her. She was so excited she piddled on my shirt.

"A puppy!" I hugged Khoi and Linh. "What's her name?"

Khoi shrugged. "She's yours, Princess Tien. You decide."

Little Nikki and I were inseparable from that point on. I loved that little dog wholeheartedly.

A few months before the end of eighth grade, I attended my first school dance. Feeling somewhat pretty in my refugee chic black ruffled skirt, white blouse, and goldenrod vest, I stood in the corner of the gymnasium pretending to hold the whole building up so that my schoolmates could have a good time. I hugged the wall, terrified of boys, especially the cute ones, content to watch the others dance to Madonna and Pet Shop Boys. Despite being the only girl at the dance with big calves and no pantyhose, I fit in with my sky-high Aqua Net hair and Cyndi Lauper punk makeup. Half the students at the school were Vietnamese refugees like me, grooving to new wave music and '80s rock. Like them, I was happiest listening to music and sneaking out of the house to get away from overbearing, overly protective, strict, paranoid, traditional parents.

An hour before the dance ended, a mysterious figure barged into the gym, pushing through the double doors like an army tank. His footsteps silenced the room, and all eyes stared at this encroaching intruder.

He grabbed my arm. "Time to go."

I pulled away and freed myself from his grip. "It's not over yet."

Binh froze. He scowled, and in a gruff whisper demanded we leave right that minute. My pride crushed, my insides hot and knotted, I stormed out, got into his Citroen Traction Avant, and slammed the door as hard as I could. A beautiful car for an ugly man.

I cried all the way home as my soon-to-be stepdad lectured. What was worse was he spoke to me in English to make sure I understood every nip of his tongue. *You are too young to be out this late. You are lucky your mom and I let you go to the dance. You must remain pious. You should not be loose around boys. Your makeup makes you look cheap. My daughter Thu was never disrespectful like you.* On and on he lashed with his fanatic insults. It took everything in me to bite my tongue and refrain from giving him a verbal beating of my own.

The following month, I cried from San Jose down to Westminster. We moved again, and I finished the last three months of eighth grade at Johnson Middle School. Yes, the school where I spent three months flirting with a boy name Dung, who ultimately regurgitated his banh mi in my mouth.

Things were about to get much worse. I felt powerless living under my stepdad's thumb and more disconnected than ever from my mom. California taught me some harsh life lessons, and I wasn't prepared to grow up so fast.

2. YOUR MAMA IS BLIND (SUMMER 1988)

Our rental home in Westminster adjoined another house on the corner of Chestnut and Park Street across from Sigler Park. The fully fenced one-story property was quite spacious with three bedrooms, two bathrooms, and a large garage. The family who lived in the other house owned the property and were also Vietnamese. They had two daughters, Leena and Loanne, who welcomed me into their sisterhood with open arms and sticky fingers.

Leena was two years younger than I was, with round-rimmed glasses that made her look innocent even when she wasn't. She had the kind of smile that lit up her whole face. Her exuberance passed through her pores. While Leena looked like her father, Tung, her sister, Loanne, was a tiny spitfire and looked like her mother, Khanh. Despite being five years younger than me, I knew better than to question her. Loanne was wicked smart, a little sarcastic, and so darn adorable. I loved both sisters equally, and while Leena acted as our moral compass, Loanne conjured our fun. It was nearly impossible to be gloomy around Leena and Loanne, but on that last Saturday, before I entered my freshman year at Westminster High School, I sunk into depression.

Nothing could have lifted my spirits, not even a visit from my sponsors from Seattle, Mr. and Mrs. Vanzwol. As the marriage of my mama and Binh approached, I became apprehensive and sullen.

"Well, hot damn, Snow," Mr. Van howled. "The California sun went and colored your face!"

"Teddy," my mama said, "you still same. You so big and strong."

Mr. Van scooped her up and crushed her in a tight embrace. "Doesn't she look great, Toots?"

Mrs. Van nodded. "I can't believe we're here in California for your wedding this Saturday. It seems like yesterday we were at Diep's wedding to Donald."

I poked my head into the kitchen and jumped on Mr. Van's back, covering his eyes with my cupped hands spreading my fingers so he could cheat. "Guess who?"

He played along. "Too heavy to be Dolly and too light to be Tree. Binh, is that you?"

Mrs. Van and Mama laughed, but Binh winced. I knew I was not behaving like a proper girl, and I was too old to be jumping on an old man's back. Still, this was Mr. Van, the man who had rescued our family from the refugee camp in Indonesia, the man who used to sing me songs while I fell asleep on his lap, the man I was convinced was Santa Claus when I caught him jingling bells outside his house one Christmas Eve.

"I'll give you a clue," I said. "I was born Thuy-Tien, grew up as Dolly, and am now…"

"Christine," Mr. Van said with confidence.

I slid off his back only to be jostled like a bag of rice. His left arm curled around my waist as he lifted me so that I was eye to eye with him. Without warning, Mr. Van brushed his rough, white beard up and down my cheeks until I begged for mercy. It was good to have them there, and I missed them more than I realized.

We gathered around the kitchen while Mama prepared spring rolls. I washed the basil, perilla leaves, lettuce, and mint while Mrs. Van offered to cut up the cucumbers and keep an eye on the vermicelli noodles cooking on the stove.

Mr. Van and Binh went to the dining room to enjoy some cognac. Binh was a big fan of Hennessy VSOP for its vanilla aroma and oaky, spicy taste with a fruity finish. He boasted it was the best and only cognac he served to special guests.

"Mr. Van is not a guest," I mumbled under my breath. "He's family."

"Catherine," my mama said, "please do not cook rice noodle all way. We want little bit chewy."

"Al dente," Mrs. Van said. "Got it."

"I so excited you come," Mama said as she ripped the heads off the prawns and peeled the shells. She threw the heads and shells into a pot of boiling water, then added salt and half an onion.

"Why do you put the shells in the pot?" I asked.

"The shell and onion add flavor and sweetness to shrimp," Mama answered. She spoke English for Mrs. Van's sake.

The three of us prepped the ingredients for the spring rolls and sat down with Binh and Mr. Van to enjoy a light dinner. With the wedding in four days, Mama didn't want to eat anything heavy or that would make her feel bloated.

Binh smacked his lips, chewed with his mouth open, and inhaled the food. Did he even taste it? My mama believed it was a compliment to the chef to eat like a pig, but I found it annoying. Mr. and Mrs. Van had well-mannered dining etiquette, and Mama was so dainty and graceful in her movements. I imagined us sitting at a candlelit dinner speaking proper English like the British royals while Binh the oinker slurped from his trough at the end of the table.

Binh leaned back and patted his stomach. "Very nice." He'd eaten five fat spring rolls in ten minutes.

I rolled my eyes. "I am barely done with my second roll."

"Eat slowly," Binh said. "You don't want to get fat."

To add insult to injury, Binh took my mama's roll, fed her a bite, then finished it for her.

"Dolly, I mean Christine," Mr. Van said, "has always been skin and bones. Remember, Toots, when we picked them up at the airport?" Mrs. Van dipped her spring roll in the hoisin sauce and took a bite just as Mr. Van posed the question. "Well, I remember it like it was yesterday. Lord have mercy, Tree was a pole, and Dolly looked like a real-life rag doll, so frail and tiny."

"And Snow was the most beautiful thing," Mrs. Van said. "I remember thinking your skin was so creamy, like milk."

My beautiful mother laughed. "I hide from sun. Too dark not pretty in Vietnamese culture. And sunspot too ugly." She pronounced "ugly" in three syllables uh-guh-lee. I smiled.

"Now, she's so tan," I said. "Must be all the hard work she has to do outside for the business."

I wondered if Binh noticed the little jab I made for making my mama work so hard on the ceramics. Mama dreamed of going to school to get her Oriental medical doctor (OMD) degree. She wanted to learn about herbal medicine and use acupressure and acupuncture to treat pain. Instead, she helped Binh build the family business. I don't know how he expected to make money when he gifted so much of it away. Each time he gave someone a vase to earn favor or climb the social ladder with someone influential, I cringed. There went a vase that I meticulously handpainted. Oh, and there went three-hundred dollars as he gave away an elephant statue that Mama painted.

My mama said you had to spend money to make money and give away free samples to get free advertising. I had argued a potato chip was a free sample, not a whole bag of chips. Sometimes I thought she was blind because she was in love. She always had a reason or explanation, but to me, they sounded like excuses. Would I think this way if I were in love?

I went into the kitchen to clear my mind and took a break from Binh's loud "ah" each time he sipped his cognac. I came back with a few sodas the Vanzwols had brought over and offered them to our guests. "Would you like a Mountain Dew?"

My mama burst out laughing. We all looked confused. What was so funny?

"Má mày đui!" Mama chuckled.

I said, "Mountain Dew," and she heard, "Má mày đui," which meant "Your mama is blind." Neither of us could stop laughing. When I finally caught my breath, I explained to my sponsors. We laughed together, even Binh, and from that moment on, the green can was forever known as the "Your mama is blind" soda.

Mrs. Vanzwol's twin sister, Ms. Katrina, and her husband, Mr. Jean-Adrien, arrived early the next day while I slept. I dreamed of a man sitting under a tree on the beach playing a string instrument with his bow. His face was handsome and familiar. My cousin Tree swam in the ocean with the blue crabs.

I woke with a start at the sound of glass shattering in the kitchen and loud voices outside my bedroom door.

"Life with this minx has never been better."

I recognized the voice and accent. I knew only one Frenchman, and it was Mr. Jean-Adrien. I scurried out of my room to greet them, hoping they brought presents for me.

"Dolly!" Ms. Katrina exclaimed. She hugged me fiercely while I inhaled her intoxicating perfume, Chanel No. 5.

Glamorous as ever, Ms. Katrina wore a mauve summer dress with a thin fuchsia patent leather belt that accentuated her small waist and round hips. She colored her hair a warm copper blonde and wore it straight with blunt bangs. While most women had mall bangs, Ms. Katrina dared to be different with her bold fashion sense. Mr. Jean-Adrien's attire was always classic and masculine. He had grown his hair out since I last saw him and looked like the dashing actor, Roger Moore, in the James Bond movies.

"Is something broken?" I asked. "I heard glass breaking."

"Oui," Mr. Jean-Adrien confirmed. "Je te présente mon ami, Chef Tuan." He pointed to a Vietnamese gentleman in the kitchen standing next to my mama. He was a stout one, and I wasn't sure if he was built from fat or muscle.

"Chef Tuan is our wedding present to your mom and Binh," Ms. Katrina said. "Your mom was so excited she dropped a dish. Chef Tuan will be here for two weeks to cook for you and teach your mom some basics."

"Wow," I said. "That's a cool present."

The doorbell rang, and from the living room window, I saw a man and woman fussing over each other's hair. Mama flew to the front of the house and threw open the door.

"Sky!" Mama cried. "Magdaleine!"

"Snow!" They exclaimed in unison and embraced my mama with magnanimous joy.

"I thought you not come," Mama said. "Oh. My. Good. Nest. You having baby!" Mama touched Ms. Magdaleine's round stomach. "Why you not tell me? Shame on you. You have boy. I know. See? It round and high."

The adults spent the entire day catching up on life. Ms. Katrina got me a makeup kit and Uncle Skyler gave us smoked copper river salmon in a nice wooden box with tribal designs on the lid. Mr. and Mrs. Vanzwol came over minutes after Binh came home from work. It was one happy reunion while Chef Tuan slaved in the kitchen. I was his prep cook while the adults lounged and reminisced about Mr. Donald and Auntie Diep's colorful wedding two years ago.

"Are they coming to the wedding?" I asked. "Are they bringing Jason, Ricky, and Hung?"

My mama nodded. "They will be here tomorrow. They are driving down."

"Anyone else?" I asked. "What about your old boss, Mr. Cushing? What about Brother Tree and Sister Kelly? Is Sister Kelly's family coming?"

"Only your cousin, Tree, and his wife are coming," Binh answered. "And of course their daughters, Holly and Honey."

I wanted to tell Binh I wasn't asking him and my mama could answer for herself. Instead, I asked, "Did you not invite them?" My spiteful jab implied he was selfish and thoughtless. Binh ignored my question.

Maybe my teenage hormones took charge, but after he humiliated me at the school dance, I lost respect for him. The anger and embarrassment still lingered. Even when he was nice, I could not accept it at face value and believed he was manipulating me somehow. How could my mama not see he was wrong for her? For us?

"So are you going to be the flower girl?" Ms. Magdaleine asked me.

"I'm too old to be—"

"No, our neighbor's daughter, Loanne, is going to be the flower girl," Binh answered. "And one of my friend's sons will be the ring bearer."

"Then you must be your mom's maid of honor," Magdaleine said.

"There won't be—"

Binh cut me off again. "We are not going to have a best man or maid of honor. We are already married on paper. The reception is where we will formally present ourselves as husband and wife."

My jaw dropped. When had this happened? I could tell by the

murmurs and raised eyebrows that everyone was equally stunned. Mama insisted it was a mutual decision since they both had been married before and did not want an elaborate wedding.

Everything about this approach was wrong to me. The contempt seeped in deeper and consumed me. My mother might be blind to his manipulations, but I would be her eyes. I was determined to expose him for the narcissistic fraud I believed him to be.

A motley crew of people spilled out of a Lincoln Town Car in front of our house and strolled up the driveway. One had her hair in pigtails and wore roller skates with pom poms on top. I could not believe my eyes. Before they rang the doorbell, I flung the door open.

Auntie Diep clutched Mr. Donald for dear life as he steadied her. She wore a green romper with knee-high socks and a gold, sequined fanny pack around her waist. Big sunglasses covered her small face and had slipped halfway down the bridge of her nose.

Auntie Diep reached for me. "Ơi, Thủy-Tiên, help me."

I laughed. "Hello, Auntie." Our Homestead Apartments neighbor hadn't changed one bit. I raised an eyebrow to Hung. "Why is your mom in skates?"

Hung smiled. He looked the same, only taller and thicker and with a deeper voice. "Mom thinks California is all about roller skating Santa Monica Pier, so she's been practicing."

Mr. Donald still looked like Phillip Drummond from the show *Diff'rent Strokes,* and his son Ricky hadn't changed other than some facial hair. Jason was still knock-kneed. Seeing them felt like home, and homesickness welled up in me like a fountain.

"Ói zòi oi!" Oh my God! Auntie Diep exclaimed when she saw my mama in the hallway.

"Trời đất ơi!" Oh heaven and Earth! My mama called back.

The two of them squealed and hugged tightly, swaying back and forth, talking animatedly as if on a mission to share every detail in five minutes. They Vietnamesed with each other as if none of us existed.

Shortly after their arrival, Brother Tree and his family arrived. All was right with the world in that brief moment. The next day was the wedding reception, and while I knew it would be egregious, I took comfort in knowing tomorrow was not today.

3. TWO'S COMPANY (SUMMER 1988)

Tree broke a teacup. He had one too many cognacs and a whole pack of cigarettes. Sister Kelly kept hitting him as if her little fists would magically make him sober up.

"It's not a party until something breaks," Mr. Van said.

Everyone but Sister Kelly roared and resumed eating, drinking, and karaokeing. It was good to see my mama laugh. She held court with Magdaleine, Ms. Katrina, Mrs. Van, Auntie Diep, and Sister Kelly. Men huddled in one area and women in the other. I entertained Jason, Hung, little Holly, and Honey, and my neighbors, Loanne and Leena, who came over for a few hours to play. I wanted to stay up late and partake in the fun, but Binh put his foot down, and Mama agreed. Both treated me like I was still in elementary school.

I stormed off to bed like a good little girl, but who could sleep with all the chatter and bad singing? Mama and Binh karaoked to the lyrics of "You're a Woman, I'm a Man" by Bad Boys Blue.

Brother Tree and Sister Kelly left first. Little Holly was four years old and had passed out long ago, but Honey, who was two, sat wide awake. She teetered between the dominions of cranky exhaustion and an energized high.

By morning, sunshine filtered into my bedroom, and its warm rays gently woke me. I listened for movement outside my room but heard nothing. I assumed all our out-of-town guests made it back to their hotels safely and nursed a hangover.

Soon, it was showtime, and I wanted the day to end before it even started.

Mama hummed the song "More Than I Can Say" in the kitchen. I scooped my dog, Nikki, into my arms and exited the room. She leaped out of my arms and scratched at the door.

"Good morning, Mama."

"How did you and Nikki sleep?" Mama asked.

I watched Nikki do her business in the backyard while I picked at the soggy egg rolls on the counter. "Not so good."

"I am sorry we were so loud. It was fun to see everyone." Mama hand-washed the glassware and let them drip-dry in the dishwasher.

I let Nikki inside and gave her the last morsel of my egg roll before serving her rice and kibble. "Is Binh passed out from all the Hennessy and Heineken?"

"He is running errands and checking on the restaurant for tonight's reception."

I opened a two-liter bottle of Mountain Dew and drank straight from the plastic mouthpiece.

"Má mày đui for breakfast?" Mama asked. We shared a giggle at her reference to Mountain Dew as "your mama is blind."

"Are you excited about the wedding reception today?" I asked.

Mama stopped wiping the counters and looked at me with a serious expression. "I want you to know he makes me happy, and I want you to try to get along with Bác Bình. I know you are not used to having a man in our lives, and you now have to compete for my time—"

"But he—"

I wanted to tell her it was he who should try to respect me and not treat me like a rotten child.

Mama held up her hand to silence me. "I want you to call him 'Dad' and—"

I took a step back and vehemently shook my head. "No way."

I picked up Nikki and held her close as if she needed my protection. In reality, she created a barrier between Mama and me. It was my heart that needed protection. All my life, it had been just the two of us. She always gave me one-hundred percent of herself. She doted on me, protected me, and saved me. I wanted nothing to change. She lived for me, and I lived for her. Couldn't she see that I was not ready for her to have a life where I was not the center of it? She didn't need anyone else to make her happy because I could do that. That was my job. I didn't want any man standing between us. I wanted to remain a child forever, and I missed the times when it was just Mama and me sharing stories and experiencing new adventures together.

My stomach churned, and my legs trembled. Mama had betrayed me. I suddenly hated California and our new beginnings there. I missed my friends back home. I planned to convince Mr. Van to take me back to Seattle with them after the reception. He had a soft spot for me and could never say no to his little Dolly. If that didn't work, I could hitch a ride back with Auntie Diep and Donald.

"Thuỷ-Tiên," Mama said, "you do not understand all the sacrifices I have made for us to be here, and I want nothing more than for us to be happy. Your cousin Tree has found his happiness, and it is our turn. We deserve it."

I clenched my fist and said under my breath, "My name is Christine now."

My mama sighed. She resumed wiping the counters but did not resume humming. I won the battle. She turned her back to me and collected the items to toss in the trash. I left her in the kitchen with her thoughts while I slammed the bedroom door and let the tears fall.

"I hate him!" I screamed. I hugged Nikki and pulled out my diary from underneath the mattress.

Diary, I can't stand him!!! Everything about him makes me want to smash his face, from the way he chews his food to the way he shoots his snot. I can see right through him, that narcissistic bastard. Today is their wedding. No, their reception. They fucking got married already without telling anyone. My mama has no clue. She is blinded by love. If I have to run away to free myself from his tyranny and strict, stupid rules, I will.

To know you is to swallow death.
I will not yield until my last breath.

To bow to you is a seal of doom.
I'll lie down for truth in my tomb.

I will not bend to the man that breaks.
His charms, his money, all but fakes.

Empty are his vessels in this harbor, this dock
For he is but a fucking cock-a-fucking-doodle-maniac-doo-doo!!!!!!!!!

I HATE YOU!

Strangers who walked alongside one another in different realms…that was Mama and me that evening. She had never shone so beautifully as she did that night, and if my heart had not been rotten with malice and ill will, I would have found the evening breathtaking. Dressed in a stunning, currant berry red *áo dài*, speckled with luminous honey-colored paisley patterns, and adorned in eighteen-carat gold jewels, she graced the floor with poise, elegance, and glamour. She was exquisite. My stepdad looked sharp, I had to admit, in his dark blue suit. They went from table to table welcoming their guests and taking photos. When people clinked their glasses with the silverware, they obliged by kissing. Behind them Loanne wore her traditional Vietnamese dress, looking adorable as always. The ring bearer was a little boy I had never met, dressed in a male version of the áo dài. He was cute in an odd way, very pale and sickly-looking. He was maybe eight years old with an old man's face and youthful skin.

I chose to wear black on their special day. I was in mourning. I had lost my mama to someone else. Binh glared at me when he saw my dress. I had gotten a rise out of him and knew he was furious. My insolence and defiance, coupled with my chastising of his blue suede shoes, compounded the resentment in the air. I sat at the round table that seated eight people with Auntie Diep, Mr. Donald, their three boys, and the Vanzwols. Next to us were Ms. Katrina, Mr. Jean-Adrien, Uncle Skyler, Ms. Magdaleine, Brother Tree, Sister Kelly, and their girls. Love and family surrounded me, yet I had never felt more alone. I didn't know where I belonged anymore. Everyone had someone, and they were moving on with their lives. Not me. I didn't feel Vietnamese, and I didn't look American. My parents expected me to be the model minority student with straight A's and to play the piano, but instead, my last report card was riddled with B's and C's. I blamed it on moving two-thirds of the way into the school year and the disruption of the status quo. Soon, I would be a freshman in a new high school, and I feared being ostracized for my smallness.

I didn't want to be a doctor, a lawyer, or an engineer. I was certainly not a musical prodigy, and math was my weakest subject. English and history were my favorite subjects, but what did that matter? I failed my mama in every way. Why bother trying?

The night went by in a blur. I spent the evening stuffing my face so I didn't have to talk. The Chinese seafood restaurant they chose had amazing salt and pepper prawns and the best garlic onion crab. Each table had red envelopes filled with cash that Loanne received for the bride and groom in a lacquered box. Money was always given at weddings, funerals, and birthdays to help with expenses. When Mama and Binh arrived at our table, Mr. Van gave a speech.

"Snow, Binh," Mr. Van said. "You both have come a long way, and we are so happy for you both. Congratulations!"

Murmurs of "cheers" and "vô" escaped jovial lips as Auntie Diep initiated the glass clinking. The bride and groom indulged us and kissed. Mrs. Van dropped a wedding card in a white envelope into Loanne's box, and I noticed Binh's disapproval by the nanosecond of his frown. White was the color of death and reserved for funerals in the Vietnamese culture. Giving a white card was considered bad luck. Hopefully, there was a generous check in the envelope to counter the bad juju.

As the night wore on and the adults danced, I amused myself by laughing at the discord of the band and the uncoordinated movements of people swaying to the rhythms of tango and pop music. Hung, Ricky, and I stole a few swigs of champagne when no one was looking, and by the time my mama and stepdad danced their solo waltz, I felt loose and buoyant.

I grabbed a rose from the centerpiece and secured the stem with my teeth. I cha-chaed to the dance floor, wedged myself between them, and slide-stepped with my mama. She laughed and waltzed with me around the room, leaving Binh alone without a partner. The guests laughed.

"Everyone," Binh said, "please, come, join us on the floor."

From that point on, I had a ball. A little drunk and a little invincible, my inner fierce came out, and I focused on the music. The band took a break, and the sounds of Modern Talking stormed the speakers. Their songs "You're My Heart, You're My Soul" and "Brother Louie" got us all up on our feet. The moment Lynda Trang Đài's song "Daddy Joe" came on, people went wild. Auntie Diep and Donald were footloose and fancy-free. They jigged and gyrated while Auntie Diep's dress lit up and flashed like LED Christmas lights.

New wave music was very much alive and thriving in our refugee world.

I wanted to know how many red envelopes Mama received last night and if they received enough cash to cover the wedding expenses. I headed to the kitchen but paused when I heard Binh and her arguing.

Binh paced in front of the living room window. "She is so hostile toward me. Everything is so dramatic with her, from her makeup to her clothes to the way she stares at me."

I ducked into the hallway closet and crouched out of sight to eavesdrop.

Mama defended me. "She is a teenager going through some changes. Be patient and show her kindness. Show her love. She will come around."

"Do you think I should take her for a ride in the Citroen and spend some time with her?"

I held my breath. I hoped she'd insist he leave me alone and let me "come around" at my own pace and on my terms. Instead, she agreed to his idea. She failed me and disappointed me.

I slumped back on my bottom and bumped a box behind me. A stack of magazines slid onto my lap. There were photos of half-naked women on the covers. I surveyed one of them. *Hustler.* XXX-Star Spectacular. August 1988. The price was $4.50. I tossed it aside and picked up another magazine. *Playboy.* Entertainment for Men. The price was $4.00. My eyes flew open wider than my mouth as I flipped through the pages. I gathered the magazines to put back in the box. Inside, I found a few VHS cassettes with covers depicting more scantily dressed women.

"Maybe I can take her to Little Saigon, show her our shop at the Phước Lộc Thọ mall, and have lunch there." My stepdad's voice sounded closer. I froze and held my breath, not making a sound until the coast was clear.

The thought of spending the day with my least favorite person in the world at the Asian Garden Mall made me want to run away with the circus or slit my wrist. Unfortunately, it was settled, and within thirty minutes, we cruised along Bolsa Avenue, just him and me. Music filled the void. My thoughts wandered to the magazines and videos I found. I shuddered. I knew Binh's secret. What would I do with it? A Cheshire smile spread across my face.

"It is nice to see you smile for once," my stepdad said.

"I have something to smile about," I said.

"Good."

We pulled into the parking lot of the Asian Garden Mall, a large, two-story building with majestic pillars out front, a statue of a happy Buddha, and white marble statues of the gods, Phước, Lộc, and Thọ. The divinity of three represented happiness, prosperity, and longevity. The entire front of the building was covered in panels of glass. Splashes of red and green adorned the building and rooftops. Large banners on either side of the entrance promoted a night market where you could buy fruits, flowers, trinkets, delectable foods, fashionable clothes, and knock-off purses.

"I think Mr. and Mrs. Van and the others would enjoy the night market," I said. "We should bring Mama later tonight."

"She would like that, although everyone left town this morning."

I whipped my head and stared at him. My mouth flew agape. "Why didn't they say goodbye?"

"They did. Remember?" Binh asked. "Cô Điệp went to the Santa Monica Pier today, and then they were going to slowly make their way back to Seattle."

There went my plans to fly back with my sponsors or hitch a ride with my auntie and Donald. "I guess I was so tired last night."

"You mean drunk?" Binh stopped by the escalator and leaned in. "I know you had some alcohol at our reception."

I shrugged. "Mama lets me sip her beer and wine all the time." I stepped onto the escalator and rode up to signal that the conversation was over.

On the second floor of the mall, our ceramics shop nestled in the corner overlooking the parking lot. Prime real estate. Binh unlocked the doors and held one open for me. The bright natural light coming in from the large windows filled the room.

"Business must be good if we can afford this space," I commented.

Arranged neatly throughout the store on the floor were statues and large vases, all hand-painted by Binh, Mama, or me. Customers could choose from an assortment of silk flowers on display to arrange themselves, or for an extra fee, trust us to make the floral arrangements for them. I was getting good at sticking moss and plastic stems into green foam and presenting them as one-hundred-dollar centerpieces. We used all kinds of flowers, from birds of paradise to lotus blossoms, irises to magnolias, and tiger lilies to calla lilies. On the shelves were figurines, floral centerpieces, and smaller vases. I picked up one of the vases I had painted and admired my work.

"You have steady hands and a good eye for detail," Binh said.

On both sides of the vase were carvings of a bride and groom in their traditional wedding garments, holding hands and looking into each other's eyes. I lifted my vase and turned it over to see the bottom. My initials TT were painted underneath in thick, black paint. I should have signed it Christine.

"Do you love your mother?" Binh asked. I scoffed. What a stupid question. "I love your mom, and it is important to her that we get along. Do you think we can start over?"

"Stop treating me like a child," I said. "Don't be condescending, and stop making decisions for me. I have a brain and an opinion, you know."

"I will try," Binh said. "Do we have a deal?" I nodded. "I would like to be a father to you. Do you think you can call me 'Dad'?"

His question grated me. My back stiffened. I shut down and built up my wall again. "I don't even call my father 'Dad.' The day I call you father is the day the Berlin Wall comes crumbling down. You can be my mama's husband, but you will never be my dad. I don't need a father."

My stepdad crossed his arms over his chest. "Your tone is very disrespectful. Your mother would be ashamed of you speaking so rudely to your elders."

I pivoted on my heel and headed toward the mall exit. "Take me home."

Music filled the void again on the drive home. Binh gripped the steering wheel the entire way. I sat in the backseat and drilled holes in his head with my eyes. High school was around the corner, and I could not wait to free myself from him.

###

Diary, you won't believe this. I found porn in the closet. Of course, they belong to him. Who else would they belong to? What a dirty old man. He asked me to call him "Dad." No fucking way. I'll be cordial to him for my mama's sake. I'll even be respectful. Hell, I'll even be the perfect daughter and get straight A's this year. One way or another, though, I'm going back to Seattle, with or without Mama. I need a job first.

Hell hath no fury for the fury lies within me.
I hear, I know, I speak, I see.
Where two's company and THREE's an asshole.
And in this game of life where pain is the toll,
Only angels and devils sent down down down…
Only sewer rats and pennywise clowns clowns clowns…
They see the cloud with the silver-lined dagger
Disguised as prominent but soon the beggar.

4. A LESSON ON RACISM (FALL 1988)

Westminster High School (WHS) had a reputation for being a bad school with gangs and cretins. If you weren't Asian or Hispanic, you were in the bullied minority. To circumvent that you had to be a cheerleader or a jock. The rumor at rival schools in Orange County was that half of us at WHS were associated with the Triads, the Yakuzas, or the Black Dragons. The misconception that all Asians looked alike meant we could claim to be Chinese yesterday, Japanese today, and Vietnamese tomorrow. The other half of the school was Hispanic, which meant you were associated with one of the crazy brothers, Los Vatos Locos.

Racial slurs were part of everyday conversation. Spics, wetbacks, and lawn mowers versus gooks, dinks, and chinks. Over eighty percent of the students received free or reduced-price lunches. If you weren't a refugee imported from Southeast Asia or a Mexican who crossed the border, then surely you were with the Crips, Bloods, or KKK. These were the misconceptions I had as I entered my freshman year at Westminster High School.

I had a plan, though, to survive the first year and maximize my time away from home. I helped run the Vietnamese Student Association, was on the yearbook committee, took honors classes, joined the beginning band and played the trumpet, joined the Spanish Club, and made the badminton team. By the end of ninth grade, I had straights A's, was fairly popular, ranked number one in girls' doubles on my badminton team, and was initiated into the Pomona Boys, a street gang that wasn't nearly as organized as the Black Dragons but had street cred for being a menace to society.

I had a few hard lessons on racism in the first couple of months at school. My parents didn't get their act together in time for me to qualify for free or reduced-price lunches, so I brought my own. On day one I sat alone with my *thịt kho tàu*, a braised pork and egg dish simmered in a clay pot until caramelized and tender. It was typically served over rice. Chef Tuan helped my mama perfect this dish, and it was one of my favorites. I opened my lunchbox, and a sour odor assaulted my nose. I quickly put the lid back on, but it was too late.

"Gross," Mean Girl said. "What died in your lunch? Smells like feet."

Her friend laughed. "Probably chicken feet. It's what they eat."

She and her friends fled the area. They looked back and pointed at me as they joined another table. My mama had packed pickled cabbage and radishes in my lunch. The pungent smell of vinegar in the California heat nearly rotted my nasal cavity and liquefied my eyes. I starved that day and cried in the bathroom. I threw my whole lunch in the girls' restroom, hoping the smell would blend in with the usual bathroom smells.

A month later I had a hard time opening my locker. Flustered, I tried the combination half a dozen times before I gave up and kicked the locker next to mine.

"¿Cuál es su problema?" A short, pudgy girl leaned against the lockers and asked me what was my problem. She challenged me to answer. My eyes widened and I stared at the odd-looking person in front of me. She had long black hair, a cute face, and pretty legs, but the rest of her features didn't match. Somebody had "Mrs. Potato Headed" her wrong. Her torso made me think of an avocado trying to fit into a peanut shell. The jeans held her stomach in and made her waist small, yet she had more rolls on her than a King's Hawaiian bakery. Pudgy Potato Head looked me up and down and snickered. "Puta."

I knew enough Spanish from telenovelas to know she called me a whore. Thanks to Mrs. Swenson's Spanish class, I countered. "Estas loca en la cabeza." *You're crazy in the head.*

Pudgy Potato Head jabbed her pointer finger at my chest and touched the tip of my scar where I had open-heart surgery. "¿Qué?" She spewed angry words in Spanish that I struggled to comprehend. The only two phrases I understood were "come mierda" and "puta madre" meaning "eat shit" and "motherfucker."

Thankfully, her boyfriend rescued me. Nearly six feet tall and looking like the Spanish version of John Stamos and Rick Springfield, he cast his sexy smile my way and winked with his hazel eyes. He wrapped his arm around Potato Head's neck and leaned down to kiss her. He immediately pacified her anger, and together they walked away, leaving me to feel like an insignificant flea.

From that day on, I was obsessed with him. Being on the yearbook committee meant I had access to names and photos. I had the biggest crush on Julio the entire year, but his potato head girlfriend, Luz, was always in the way. Her name meant "light," but I called her "Loose."

I joined the Spanish Club with an ulterior motive of moving into Julio's circle, under the guise of wanting to practice Spanish. I was the only Asian person in the club, and by the second semester, I faded away unnoticed.

I unexpectedly found my niche when I joined the Vietnamese Student Association (VSA). In Seattle, I knew only one other Vietnamese kid, our neighbor's son, Hung. In Westminster, we were a colony of rabbits, but I was convinced they were not my kind of people. The girls had Aqua Net hair with towering bangs and dressed in black while the boys wore layered, new wave, punk clothes, and pointy shoes. Most of them spoke loudly with thick accents, and I didn't want to be associated with the FOB's, the Fresh Off the Boaters, who hadn't assimilated into American culture as I had.

I yearned to belong to something. I didn't talk like them or dress like them, but at least I looked like them. That first VSA meeting opened my eyes and taught me it was I who was racist.

"Welcome to the Vietnamese Student Association," Van said. "Here, fill this out."

She handed me a membership questionnaire asking for my name and phone number, what ideas I had for fundraisers, what activities and foods I enjoyed, and my favorite movie, song, artist, and sport. Through the VSA, I learned we all had the same frustrations with our parents, who coerced us to fit into a standard box where family traditions, culture, and beliefs were institutions of life. Meanwhile, we desperately wanted to experiment and compete to be individuals with our ideals and independence. It was the American way, and we were Americans. We liked Taco Bell, McDonald's, and Godfather's Pizza. We hated curfews, being seen but not heard, and getting scolded for public displays of affection with the opposite sex.

I came to understand that my fellow Asian-Americans were loud not because they were fresh off the boat country bumpkins but because they had fun. They laughed, they teased, they bantered, and they were great storytellers. I got caught up in the frenzy and found my niche. We liked the same music, enjoyed the same foods, laughed at the same jokes, and wrinkled our noses at our parents' old-world beliefs. In time, I was an important member of the VSA and helped Van lead the club through car washes, cultural fairs, potlucks, study groups, and social outings.

The school gazette advertised tryouts for a new badminton team. I poured over the blurb and failed to hear Mrs. Swenson call my name in Spanish class. Someone tapped my arm. It was Trina, a classmate.

"Christine," Mrs. Swenson said, "would you please kick us off in a song?"

The only song I had memorized in Spanish was "La Bamba," because it was repetitive and simple. Plus, I had recently watched the movie starring Lou Diamond Phillips as Ritchie Valens. Mrs.Swenson queued up the music and displayed the lyrics on the overhead transparency projector. The class sang one song after another for our Spanish lesson that day.

Trina and I quickly became friends. Like me, she was the only child of immigrant parents and put in the extra credits to get straight A's. She was smart, shy, and grounded. We were a good team and often partnered up in chemistry, science lab, and Spanish. I trusted her with my secrets. She knew I loathed my stepdad and crushed hard on Julio. We talked about everything and nothing. Many times, we walked home together and spent time in her bedroom listening to music or hanging out in my room playing with Nikki.

Like me, she was close to her mother and was raised without a strong father-figure in her life. Between the two of us, however, I was wilder, louder, and more social. I wore makeup and was not afraid to speak my mind or challenge authority. Trina and Van became my closest girlfriends, but my friendships with them were separate. With Van, I could be crass, foul-mouthed, vulgar, and boy-crazy. We loved '80s heavy metal and appreciated Skid Row and Poison. We lived day by day and acted foolishly and impulsively. I took risks when I was with Van. I was guarded when I was with Trina. She brought out the softer, more studious, well-mannered side of me. We listened to Madonna and Whitney Houston, strived for perfection on our homework, and dreamed of the future. I was two different people at times.

###

Too uncoordinated to try out for cheerleading and too small to play volleyball, I chose badminton thinking, how hard could it be? The school had never had a badminton team before. The new program had new coaches and competitive divisions for singles and doubles, junior varsity, and varsity. I walked into the gym and sat down with the other hopefuls. Coaches Marcelo and Zhang were easy on the eyes, and I knew I had to make the team. They went over the rules, history, and terminologies of the sport then demonstrated ways to serve, smash, and move within the tramlines. Their rally was impressive as I watched both coaches play a real men's singles game. The shuttlecock moved so fast at times I could not see it. Coach Marcelo scored the winning point with a kill to Zhang's body, and I pledged allegiance right then and there that I'd make badminton my sport.

Tryouts were tough. I rotated from court to court and played girls' singles, girls' doubles, and mixed doubles. Both coaches floated around the room with their clipboards, jotting down notes and nodding their approval or frowning their dismay.

When Marcelo shouted, "Drop shot," I finessed the shot and watched the birdie fall over the net into my opponent's court.

When Zhang screamed, "Drive," I sent the shuttlecock over the net like a bird shot out of a cannon and hit my opponent squarely in the neck.

I served when told to serve, and I flicked when told to flick. After two hours, I glistened and smelled like fish sauce.

The next day, I made the team and partnered up with Amy Chen to play girls' doubles. Amy was from Hong Kong. She had an older sister who looked nothing like her. Whereas Amy was petite with an athletic build and wore fashionable clothes from United Colors of Benetton, her sister, Mina, was overweight and introverted and preferred baggy and simple clothes. Amy and I quickly became friends and often surprised each other with gifts…new Yonex or Black Knight rackets or new feather shuttlecocks when ours fell apart. We restrung each other's rackets, and we coordinated our clothes so we'd look like twins.

During competitions, I'd yell, "Yours," or she'd say, "Mine," and when we scored, we high-fived with our rackets. We finished the season ranked number one in the girls' JV doubles division and earned a jacket.

All was falling into place, and my life was perfect until I met Jade, Mad Dog, and Juice. The Pomona Boys were anything but boys.

5. MISS THE BOAT (SPRING 1989)

She walked into my life like a fresh, inexplicable bruise, looking nebulous and mysterious. One day she wasn't there, and the next thing I knew, she appeared in beautiful swirls of blue, purple, and red. I never noticed her in my history class, but I suppose it was because I sat in the front row, right in front of Mr. Hamamoto's podium where a large poster of Clint Eastwood stared at me.

Mr. Hamamoto was a small Japanese man who didn't have much going for him in terms of looks. He was short, balding, and below-average looking. He was however intelligent and had an infectious sense of humor. He spoke to his students as if we were family, with respect, with compassion, with high expectations because he saw our potential, and he wasn't afraid to say "shit" in front of us. He was blessed with a beautiful wife who had blonde hair and was six inches taller than he was. He shared stories of their personal life and the crazy lessons they learned raising their baby daughter together. I was blessed to have fun teachers in ninth grade, which made school easy for me.

Mr. Hamamoto called students to the front of the classroom to give presentations on a historical event of our choice. "Jade, you're up next."

A Vietnamese girl from the back row slowly made her way to the front of the room and dramatically pivoted around to face the class. Her raven hair was long, jagged, layered, and thick like tar. Her black clothes, black nail polish, and thick black eyeliner made her look punk goth, but as dark and mysterious as she was, she had a light that shone through her eyes that reminded me of the grass jelly dessert of East Asia.

The rest of Jade's ensemble was full of color, from her eyeshadow and lipstick to her jewelry and Patrick Nagel pop art T-shirt peeking through her black jacket. I didn't know what to think of her. Part of me suspected she'd bomb her oral presentation, but the other part of me hoped she'd surprise us all and ace it.

"My presentation is in the form of poetry." Jade's voice was soothing and calm, almost hypnotic. Her poem was titled "Miss the Boat."

Gunfire screams and the roof collapses.
The sky ablaze with anger, I think I hear her.
Death. She comes to me. She's coming for you.
Death is but a prostitute. Pain is her pimp.
I run. My legs anchored in rot. I cannot miss the boat.

Headless soldiers stripped naked before me.
Limbless babes suckle and cling to Mother.
My sister, my brother, where are they?
Society crumbles. From ashes rise new power.
I must leave. I cannot miss the boat.

Where freedom has no footing
And truth swallows lies
I sit and wait and wait and sit
I puke and crap all over myself
Knowing I will miss the boat.

Bombs roil the air, they blind me.
Torpedoes light up the ocean floor.
Flames burn and smoke shields.
I wallow. I didn't take action, and now,
I've missed the fucking boat.

Jade stopped reading. Why had she stopped? I wanted more. I hung onto her words, hoping to catch every drip, thirsty to taste her message. I was drawn to her like a bewitched subject, afraid yet curious.

The class was quiet. I applauded. Jade looked at me, and if there was such a thing as humans imprinting on each other, then she imprinted on me. I was ready to draw a black dagger for her.

"Thank you, Jade," Mr. Hamamoto said. "What was your poem about?"

Jade gritted her teeth. "Um, it's about missing the fucking boat."

The class roared, and everyone talked over each other. Mr. Hamamoto did not appreciate her sarcasm. He shifted uneasily. He rang his cowbell, and we knew to shut up or spend an entire fifty minutes the next day writing on the chalkboard, "I will not disrupt Mr. Hamamoto's class."

"But," I said, "what part of history was this poem about?"

"Now you're missing the boat," Jade said. "It isn't about an event in time. It is time. It is history. It's every war, every missed opportunity, every time you skip dinner because you don't want to get fat. Wake up, people!"

Jade screamed the last part. She slammed her assignment on Mr. Hamamoto's podium, stormed down the aisle to the back row, and strode out the door. We still had twenty minutes left of class. Her temper escalated fast and left us stunned.

Jade didn't show up to class the next day, and then it was the weekend. For once, I stopped obsessing over Julio and let Jade's parasitic presence consume me.

Jade sat in the corner of the classroom and sulked like a child in timeout. I sauntered to her desk, trying to exude confidence and coolness. I wore black with a Patrick Nagel shirt underneath my faux leather jacket to impress her.

"I loved your boat poem," I said. "What inspired you to write it?"

She stared at me intensely and said, "Pomona."

"As in the city?" I asked.

"Hey, after class, you wanna get out of here?"

I shook my head, and before I could say no, Jade picked up her backpack and stood up.

"Wait," I said. "Where should I meet you after history class?"

"Taco Bell."

Mr. Hamamoto entered and blocked the doorway. "Jade, stay. Please." His eyes pleaded while his hand reached for the doorknob.

Jade stood stance to stance with Mr. Hamamoto and returned to her seat.

The hour ticked by slowly, and when the dismissal bell rang, Jade and I popped out of our seats. Instead of heading to my locker to get my lunch, I followed Jade to the parking lot.

A white Acura Integra with tinted windows and racing tires pulled up to the curb.

Jade opened the door. "You coming?"

Inside were two guys, one with pockmarks and the other with glasses. I nodded and got in. "We're going to Taco Bell?"

No one said anything. I secured my seatbelt and held my breath. I wanted to play it cool and not act like a scared sissy, but truth be told, I silently prayed I would not get kidnapped and appear on the front of a milk carton as missing.

At Taco Bell Jade paid for my lunch since I did not have any money. The four of us sat down, and I dug into my Mexican pizza, pretending not to notice that the driver, the one with the glasses, stared at me.

"You going to introduce us?" Glasses guy asked.

Jade swallowed her taco. "Mad Dog. Juice." She waved her hand at both of them. Mad Dog was the one with glasses. He looked like the boy next door with his round face and kind eyes. I didn't dare ask him his real name or why he was called Mad Dog. Juice was the pockmark guy, lanky and quiet. He had scars on his forearm and a cobra tattoo on his neck. I wondered how old they were.

"Well, I'm Christine," I said. My voice trembled, but I tried to mask it by sitting up straight and following it with a peppy statement. "Thanks for inviting me to lunch."

I had never been off campus for lunch before. A lot of students did that, but I never had money to spend. Suddenly, I wished I were sitting with Trina or Van or Amy, talking about homework, rock bands, or badminton. It was the most awkward moment of my young life.

Mad Dog stood up and slid next to me. He helped himself to a slice of my Mexican pizza. "Why are you here?"

I wasn't sure what he was asking. "Um," I stammered. "Uh…Jade invited me. Well, she asked me to meet her here but—"

"You like Poison?" Mad Dog pointed at my heavy metal bracelet.

I blushed. "Yeah, Brett Michaels is amazing."

We talked about music, cars, fashion, and school while Jade and Juice ate silently. I found it easy to talk to Mad Dog and couldn't fathom how he got that nickname.

Before long, as the weeks passed, I spent less and less time eating lunch on campus and instead joined my new friends at Taco Bell. Mad Dog was charmingly intimidating. He opened doors for Jade and me but had no problem yelling at anyone who showed disrespect. He often paid for our meals but scoffed if we didn't eat it all. He showered me with compliments and made me feel smart, empowered, and pretty. With him, it was easy to be confident and speak my mind. He was the safety net that caught me if I messed up and the big brother to the rescue if anyone was disrespectful.

Juice warmed up to me, and I warmed up to him. He was scary to look at, but his scars and tattoos were simply expressions of individualism. I found out his pockmarks were caused by acne, not chickenpox.

Jade took on the role of big sister and stood up to bullies at school for me. She'd mischievously put drops of Visine in someone's lunch if they were mean to me or nonchalantly trip them if they said something degrading. We'd laugh when her victims scurried off to the bathroom or fell flat on their faces. Jade would ask if they had a nice trip. I took pleasure in the harmless fun and came up with ways to humiliate others. It made Jade laugh and I wanted her to like me.

After a month of darting off campus to meet them for lunch or to cruise around, they showed me their true colors. At first, they dared me to steal something small at the convenience store. Over time, I got more brazen and stole money right out of people's hands. I lived a secret life. At home, I stayed out of my stepdad's way and helped the family business. I cared for my dog, helped Mama in the kitchen, and pretended everything was fine. At school, I maintained my grades, joined club activities, and played badminton. I often lied to my mama that I had practice after school or a badminton competition. When I was with Mad Dog, Juice, and Jade, we were just four kids goofing off, pushing ourselves to the limit to see how far we could go without getting caught.

Mad Dog always talked about the Pomona Boys gang, how they cruised Little Saigon, gambled illegally, participated in drive-by shootings, sex-trafficking, and drug solicitations at nightclubs, but my naivete did not put two and two together. The same thugs he referenced were the same street gang members I ate lunch with at Taco Bell.

One Saturday morning, my mama and stepdad left early for the shop at the Asian Garden Mall. I promised I would weed the garden if they let me sleep in and stay home. A hard knock at the door startled me while I was feeding Nikki. I peeked through the side window to see Mad Dog waving at me.

I opened the door. "What are you doing here? How did you know where I lived?"

"Can I come in?" he asked.

I hesitated but opened the door wider. "My parents will be home soon."

"It's time you meet the Pomona Boys," he said. "But first…"

He advanced toward me with one swift stride and grabbed my wrist. My body slammed against his, and his hot mouth pressed against my lips. His tongue—wet, sloppy, rushed, invasive—dug deep. I pushed him away and stepped back, only to be pulled back into his arms. His fingers stabbed my back, and he towered over me.

"Stop!" I yelled. I kicked him in the shin. "What the hell is wrong with you?"

Mad Dog released me, stunned. His face softened. "I'm sorry."

I exhaled and let my guard down. Big mistake. He locked the front door and took off his shirt. My heart raced. The ceiling closed in and the room spun. I panicked. I swallowed the fear in my throat. My hands balled into a fist, and I stood defiant.

"You're a little Miss Vixen, aren't you?" Mad Dog asked. It was a rhetorical question. He lunged forward, and I ran in the only direction I could—down the hallway and straight into my room. I slammed the door shut, but he pried it open before I could lock it. I frantically looked around for a weapon. What good would a diary and stuffed animal do to halt him in his tracks? No lamp, no trophy, not even a picture frame to slow him down. *Why did I not run out of the back door?*

It was a cat and mouse game, and I lost. Mad Dog pinned me down on my bed and assaulted my lips until they were bruised. The weight of his body crushed me as he groped at my chest. *Dear God, please help me.*

His dry, calloused hand slid under my T-shirt and tugged at my bra. I froze. My body and will went limp. I opened my mouth to scream but nothing came out. I could not move even though I wanted to hurl his body out the window. His power over me was too strong, and I gave up.

I stared at the ceiling while he explored my neck with his mouth. A tear escaped the corner of my eye. His hand found the tiny bow on the front of my panties, and I closed my eyes. When I opened them again, the faces of Aerosmith stared back at me. The band's lead singer, Steven Tyler, told me to get up, to fight. *I can't.* Back and forth, I had this imaginary conversation with my poster. *You can,* he said.

Mad Dog slid off the bed and stood at the foot of it. He unbuttoned his jeans and pulled the zipper down. It was now or never. Before he could slide his pants off his ankles, I summoned all my willpower and sprang out of the room. I darted for the front door. He was two steps behind me and seized my waist. I stomped on his foot, but it didn't affect him. We pushed and pulled for control, falling to the floor. I clawed at his face and punched him in the throat. His shoulder slammed into the wall.

I leaped to my feet and crushed his crotch with all the force my ninety-five-pound body could muster. He cried out in pain, anger, and surprise. I ran out of the front door and did not stop until I was on the other side of Sigler Park. On the steps of the Blessed Sacrament Catholic Church, I watched from afar as Mad Dog got in his car and sped off. Inside the church, I slumped on the bathroom floor and cried.

That night, I thought long and hard about cutting my wrists. I wanted to die as I relived that event over and over. How could I have been so stupid, so trusting, so naïve? I was angry at Jade for befriending me. I was angry at Mad Dog for what he tried to do. I hated my stepdad for being overbearing. I resented my mama for not seeing how unhappy I was at home. I blamed myself for it all.

Jade tried to talk to me the following week, but I evaded her. One afternoon after badminton practice, Jade and Mad Dog cornered me in the parking lot near the gym.

"There's Miss Vixen," Mad Dog said. He acted as if nothing had happened and we were best friends. He swung his arm around my neck. "You're one of us now. C'mon, I'll introduce you to the rest of the Pomona Boys."

I slapped his arm off me. "Get away from me."

Jade pushed Mad Dog aside. "Leave her alone."

"What?" Mad Dog cried out. "Don't be mad. It was just a test. Vixen, you passed your initiation."

"Get out of my way, Jade," I said, "if that's even your real name."

"I wasn't going to do anything to hurt you, Christine," Mad Dog said. "I just wanted to make sure you could handle yourself."

Jade laughed. "And from what I heard, you did a number on him."

I swiveled around and screamed, "You think this is funny? I fucking hate you both. You tricked me. And to think, I liked you, Jade. Get the hell away from me."

Jade let out a nervous laugh. "Give her time. She'll get over it."

Mad Dog sneered. I knew his patience wore thin. "Get in the car."

I didn't wait to find out if he was talking to me or Jade. I ran back to the gym and prayed they would not chase me. Inside, Coaches Marcelo and Zhang were packing up. Two other players waited on them, getting ready to head out. I mumbled an excuse and asked if they had recommendations on where I could take my racket to have it strung at a higher tension.

As luck would have it, they all were heading to the Big 5 Sporting Goods near my house. We piled into coach Marcelo's car. I got my racket strung, and they dropped me off at home later.

Tomorrow was another day.

6. MY LIFELINE (SUMMER 1989)

School came to an end almost as quickly as it started. Jade dropped out a few weeks after the gym parking lot incident. Her last words to me before she disappeared were, "You're the one that got away, Christine. You're lucky. Watch your back."

I had so many questions. What was her initiation like? How did she get involved in the gang? Was Jade her real name? I could not find her on the yearbook roster. I wondered how Mad Dog and Juice got their names but was thankful I hadn't stuck around long enough to find out. And just like that, the beautiful bruise that was Jade, who had appeared out of nowhere one day, vanished.

I headed into summer relieved I never saw Mad Dog again or got tangled in their web. The experience gave me a new perspective on my life. I vowed to be a better daughter, give my relationship with my stepdad another chance, and never fall for bad boys again.

In the kitchen, Mama hummed a Lionel Richie song. She squatted on the floor with a meat cleaver in her hand, decimating a chicken. "Oh good, you are awake. I need you to cut the Chinese sausage for me and wash the bok choy."

I leaned down and kissed the top of her head. "What are you making?"

"Ba mày kêu," Mama said.

"My dad called?" I asked.

"He did?" Mama asked. "When? How did he get our number?"

I was confused. "No, Mama. You said my dad called. You sad 'Ba mày kêu.'"

Mama laughed. She tipped over from her squatting position and wiped her nose with her sleeve. She picked up the chicken head and bobbed it in front of my face like a hand puppet. She laughed so hard she could barely get the words out. "Ba mày kêu. Má mày đui!"

It dawned on me she was saying, "Barbecue. Mountain Dew."

She slapped my leg, amused at her cleverness for coining the words "barbecue" and "Mountain Dew" as "your father called" and "your mama is blind."

She had me in stitches. We would get serious for a few minutes, me cutting up sausage and her marinating the chicken in ginger soy sauce until one of us cracked a smile. Then it was over. Bouts of laughter rang through our kitchen and out the window.

During moments like these, she would strike with something serious. "I want you to learn Vietnamese and stick with it this time. You are Vietnamese. You must never forget that."

I rolled my eyes and sighed. "How can I forget? You remind me all the time."

"You speak broken Vietnamese like you are still six years old. I found you a school."

The last two times Mama found me a school, I was stuck in a classroom with children who were five and six years old. Two hours every Sunday, she'd push me into the classroom like a cat going into a carrier. I was humiliated. The little kids surpassed me each week in reading, writing, and memorizing songs. I was the only teen learning the alphabet and nursery rhymes. Both times I dropped out of Sunday Vietnamese school and refused to return.

"This is a different language school," Mama said. "The lessons are taught in English and Vietnamese, and the students are teenagers. You'll be with kids your age who are at the same skill level. It is like ESL, only it is VSL." Mama chuckled at the thought of a Vietnamese girl learning Vietnamese as a second language.

I hissed at her but agreed to go only if I did not have to work at the ceramics shop. We struck a deal, and off I went on Sundays to VSL. That summer, I learned the alphabet, how to write basic words, sentence structures, and sing the national anthem of the Republic of Vietnam. A dozen of us attended the summer class. Hormones flew like crazy as we teased, flirted, and played games with one another during breaks. I was thankful I knew the basics of pronunciation, the accent marks, and the inflections associated with them. I sounded out words like a toddler learning to read. Soon I read newspapers and magazines, but I still felt illiterate. Understanding what I read was a whole other issue, one that made Mama and Binh laugh. At times I got frustrated, but then I'd hear how absurd I sounded and join in on the laughter.

My stepdad found the language school for teens, and for that I was grateful. The more I relaxed around him, the more playful he got. For my early fifteenth birthday present, Binh gave me two tickets to the Poison concert. They were on tour and came to the Long Beach Arena. I finally saw Brett Michaels live and took my friend, Van, with me. My stepdad promised I could stay for the entire concert and that he would not pull me out early. He even agreed to let me stay the night at Van's house that whole weekend since school was out. Fifteen was going to be a great year!

Everything about that concert was magical. The arena lights bounced off the walls and roof. People from all walks of life came in full makeup, ratted hair, and metal rags. I was most surprised to see men in their forties and fifties at the concert. I thought only young people in their teens and twenties enjoyed Poison. Mama gave me fifty dollars to spend on food, drinks, and a souvenir. Khoi and Tree gave me a little extra under the table as they always did, which was a good thing because the T-shirt I wanted was forty-nine dollars. After the concert, Van's cousin picked us up to take us back to her house where I would spend three nights engaging in girl talk, listening to heavy metal music, and lounging at the beach.

A little after midnight, a blue 1986 Toyota Supra pulled up in front of the arena. A young man with a short military haircut got out and gestured us over. New Wave music blared from his speakers the moment the door opened. The sounds of "Cheri, Cheri Lady" by Modern Talking lifted my spirits and revitalized my mood to keep the night going.

"That's my cousin," Van said. "Let's go."

My jaw dropped. The car shimmered under the moonlight and was bathed in the glow of concert lights. It was so waxed and buffed I could see Van's braces in the reflection when she smiled. I was afraid to touch the car, but I didn't have to. Van's cousin opened the door for me, and I climbed in the back. The car smelled nice—a swirl of musk and florals.

"What air freshener is that?" I asked.

"It's cologne," Ace said. "Obsession." Van's cousin popped in a new tape, and while we were stuck in concert traffic, the three of us absorbed the Euro-Italo Disco music of Bad Boys Blue.

"The grunion are supposed to be running this weekend," Ace said. "Want to go?"

"Now?" I asked. "It's after midnight. Aren't your parents—"

"They're out of town," Van said. "My cousin just got out of the navy, and he's staying with us for a while."

"I get to babysit," Ace said.

"We're not babies," Van said. She whipped around and tossed me some Tic Tac breath mints. "We're fifteen."

"How old are you?" I asked Ace.

He was twenty years old. He had a younger brother, Tung, who went to college in Texas. His parents were still in Vietnam, and he hadn't seen them for over ten years. One day, he hoped to return to Vietnam and build his parents a nice house. His goal was to save thirty thousand dollars to buy them the land, materials, and labor needed to build a suitable home.

Ace's and Van's families were from a village in the north but migrated south during the conflict. After the fall of Saigon, they lost everything. His parents convinced Van's father to take Tung and Ace with them out of the country. They left on a rickety old boat that was not seaworthy at all, and like my family, they settled into a refugee camp.

The Songkhla Camp, located in Thailand on the beachfront far from civilization, housed over six thousand boat people. The camp was surrounded by barbed wire and controlled by the Thai army. Thanks to the charitable work by the United Nations High Commissioner for Refugees (UNHCR) and the personal humanitarian efforts led by Father Joe Devlin, the camp had a few wells to supply fresh water for cooking, huts and barracks for sleeping and schooling, and charcoal for heating.

Ace remembered fondly of talking to Father Joe and how much he loved the priest's compassion for the Vietnamese people. It was Father Joe who organized a sponsorship for the five of them to come to America. It was because of Father Joe that Ace became a Catholic.

By the time the three of us arrived at Long Beach, it was nearly two in the morning. The moon shone bright and the grunion flopped about on the sand. Hundreds of these fish came to shore to spawn during high tide twice a month from March through August. The females dug themselves into the sand and laid their eggs, then jumped out so the males could fertilize them.

The night was warm and my clothes stuck to my skin. In the distance, other people watched the grunion run. Ace peeled off his shirt and darted into the water. Van kicked off her shoes and bobbled in after him. The two of them splashed around and demanded I join them.

"But I'm watching the fish," I yelled.

Ace dove into the waves and swam to shore. He ran toward me, and I realized he meant to carry me into the water. I dodged him but lost my footing in the sand. He charged at me, threw me over his shoulder, and waded into the water.

Slung over his shoulder, I wrapped my arms around his hard, muscular torso. The faint smell of his cologne mixed with the salty air and made me lightheaded. My stomach fluttered, and my heart pounded against my chest as I tensed my body. Ace threw me in the ocean and adrenaline flooded my body. I was not a strong swimmer and scurried to stand up. We splashed around, and both Van and I charged at him.

Ace scooped me into his arms, and I punched him in the pecs, afraid he was going to dunk me again. Instead, he placed me gently on my feet and held me. It felt like minutes, but it was mere seconds. We locked eyes, and my gaze drifted to his full lips. I wanted to kiss him.

He released me. "Let's go. I better get you girls home."

Ace was the summer love and cure for boredom I desperately wanted. We had fun that summer, and even though he was five years older than me, we didn't analyze the fact that I was a minor and he an adult. Ace was my first love, and long after we parted, the magic was still there. He cast a spell on me that brought me total bliss, deep sorrow, and layers upon layers of regret. He carved his name into my heart so deeply, I could not breathe, could not function, could not think without him. He was my lifeline, and I was his.

7. BOUNDARIES (WINTER 1989-SPRING 1990)

Nineteen-eighty-nine was an historic year. I sat with Ace on the floor, tears streaming down my face, as we witnessed the Berlin Wall coming down on that November day. Every news channel and media outlet covered the event. The thirteen-foot-tall and ninety-six-foot-long wall was built after WWII to divide the eastern and western parts of the city. Anyone caught crossing it was shot down, no questions asked. Free passage from east to west was granted on November 9 and reunification of Germany was underway. Families who had been separated for twenty-eight years hugged and cried as relief and joy filled their spirits. They danced, drank, and celebrated throughout the night while tearing the concrete wall down.

Ace wrapped his arm around my waist and pulled me to him. "Communism will collapse for Vietnam one day."

I snuggled closer to him. "I hope so. I don't remember my family back home and hope to meet them. My mama misses her brother and sister, and I know my cousin wants to see his family again too. He hasn't seen them for almost eleven years."

"How can you two breathe?" Van asked. "There's like no air between the two of you." Ace and I snuggled closer with me on his lap. She handed me a bowl of popcorn and turned on the VCR. "What movie did you rent for us?"

I wrapped my arm around Ace's neck and kissed him on the temple. "Did you get the new *Nightmare on Elm Street?*"

"Did you go to Blockbuster or Hollywood Video?" Van asked.

Ace laughed. "Yes to all three." He ran his fingers through his hair. I knew my body heat was making him hot.

I moved to the couch to sit next to Van. Ace stood and removed his shirt. I gawked at his physique. I didn't think I would ever tire of looking at him. Every day he ran and did calisthenics to stay in shape. I loved watching him do his sets of squats, crunches, pushups, planks, and dips. Over time he got used to me being the creepy girlfriend who stared all the time. He grunted and sweated while doing his exercises, while I sat on the floor, guilt-free, eating my food and drooling. I had no shame.

Ace sat on the couch with us, and I immediately put my cold feet on his stomach to soak up all his warmth. The three of us watched the horror flick and stayed up late eating ramen, drinking pop, and helping ourselves to *chè*, a Vietnamese dessert soup that came in a variety of flavors, colors, and ingredients. Some chè were served warm while others were served with crushed ice. My favorite was *chè Thái*, a fruit cocktail made with jackfruit, longans, lychees, toddy palm seeds, pandan jelly, and coconut milk. Ace preferred *chè ba màu*, which was three layers of sweet yellow mung beans, sweet red kidney beans, and green pandan jelly nestled into a lot of crushed ice and bathed in sweet coconut cream. Van went for the *chè sâm bổ lượng*, a refreshing dessert made with kelp, lotus seeds, longans, pearl barley, and red dates.

As my sophomore year rolled on, I spent less and less time at home. I did my own thing, hung out with my friends, and continued to stay busy with badminton and club activities. During the first half of the school year, Ace waited for me in his Supra a block from my school. We didn't want anyone to know about our relationship, especially since he was five years older than I was. We stole moments together before my parents came home. Most of the time, we sat at the park and talked or he helped me with homework. If we weren't kissing, we were constantly touching, whether it was my head on his lap or his leg over mine. If our hands were not touching, then our shoulders were. We were so much a part of each other that being apart was physically painful. My stomach would knot or his head would throb until we saw each other again.

Ace made me laugh. With him I felt special, loved, and beautiful. We made plans for the future. That Valentine's Day, he had a bouquet of roses and a box of chocolates waiting for me in the car. I was so in love with him I could not imagine life without him.

"Happy Valentine's Day!" I leaned over and kissed him passionately. "I didn't get you anything."

"It's okay," he said. "I'm the one with the job."

"Do you want to come to the house?" I wanted to show him my room and where I hid his love notes. I wanted him to meet my dog and show him the scrapbook I made of us. I wanted to read my love poems, and most of all, I wanted to lie in his arms.

"I don't think that's a good idea," he said.

I pleaded and pouted. "We can cuddle…" I reminded him it was Valentine's Day, and he was supposed to spoil me.

Ace laughed and gave in. "All right, but no more than half an hour. The last thing I want is to get caught alone in your room in your parents' house when they come home."

"They're not due back until five," I said. "We'll easily have an hour."

Inside my room, we listened to music and ate Valentine's Day chocolates. We dreamed of our future together and planned to marry right after my eighteenth birthday. He wanted me to remain a virgin until then.

"And while you go to college," Ace said, "I'll work and save money for our house and children."

I giggled at the thought of us having babies. "How many do you want?"

"How many can you handle?" he teased.

I counted the numbers on my fingers. "Well, counting you…"

"Me?" Ace threw me on the bed and tickled me. "Trust me, I'm no child."

I laughed until I could not breathe. Ace let up and let me catch my breath. He tenderly stroked my hair and said the three words I had been waiting to hear.

"I love you too," I said.

We kissed and let our hands wander. I wanted to explore his body and see every inch of him, but he would not let me. It frustrated me. I felt rejected.

"We can't," he said. "I want to…but…you don't want me to go to jail, do you?"

"Three years is a long time to wait," I said. I straddled his hips and pinned his arms above his head. "If you love me…"

Ace rolled over and pushed himself away from me. He stood up and collected his keys. "If I love you, I won't ruin you. This summer, you'll turn sixteen, and I'll be twenty-one, and before you know it, you'll graduate high school and go off to college. I'm not going anywhere. We'll get married and do this the right way. We'll get both of our parents' blessings, because one day when the embargo is lifted and we can safely return to Vietnam, I want to introduce you to my family. Even though my family are northerners and yours are southerners, I want our families to get along."

"They'll get along," I said. "It's not like your family was Viet Cong. We fought on the same side."

"It's not that simple," Ace said. "Babe, I'm going to be here every step of the way to make sure you get your education. That's super important to me. We can't give them any reason not to give us their blessings. Besides, I want our daughters to be proud of us."

I raised my eyebrow. "Daughters, huh?"

A smile crept on his lips and lit up his face. "I want to be smothered with little girls. They are so cute."

"Well, I want boys," I said. "I can't handle little girls, and if they grow up to be anything like me…well, payback is a bitch."

Ace pulled me to my feet. He kissed me softly. "Happy Valentine's Day. I'll see you tomorrow after school."

Ace continued to come to my house after school for weeks. He taught me card games like *tiến lên*, also called the game of Thirteen, while we listened to music. Thirteen was popular in Vietnam. Players shed their cards in ranked order, with the two of hearts being the highest and three of spades being the lowest. As each player discarded, the last one left with cards was declared the loser and had to pay up. Stakes were often high when we played together with Van. The three of us were competitive and made up ridiculous penalties for the loser. Van once had to flash her breasts to the old neighbor across the street, who was nearsighted, but that didn't make it any less embarrassing. I often lost, and the nastiest thing I had to do was chew gum for five minutes after Ace and Van already had it in their mouths.

One particular Friday night, I slept over at Van's house, and Ace came over. We played Thirteen.

Van rubbed her hands together like she was warming them in front of a fire. "Okay, guys, if Ace loses, he has to teach us to drive his car."

Ace shook his head vehemently. I squeezed his arm and grinned, bobbing my head up and down. "And if Van or I win, then we'll teach you how to roller skate."

"Perfect!" Van exclaimed.

"Wait," Ace said. "Either way, I lose!"

"Perfect!" I said and dealt each of us thirteen cards. "Sorry, honey, it's two against one. Either you learn to skate, or we learn to drive."

Van picked up her cards and smiled mischievously. She rocked to and fro. "Yes, it's time we learned."

Now, tiến lên was not a challenging game to play, but it did require a little strategy. Although Van and I never admitted to ganging up on Ace or cheating, we did squeak out a win after six rounds. The following day, on the brightest California day of our young lives, Van and I learned to drive, and Ace nearly had a heart attack teaching us.

###

Spring break had arrived. Binh, Mama, and I came home from the Presbyterian church in Garden Grove and changed out of our Sunday clothes. Binh tended to the garden while my pup, Nikki, supervised. Mama and I busied ourselves in the kitchen.

"You have been happy lately," Mama said. "School is going well?"

I took the carrots out of the fridge and chopped them into one-inch pieces. "School is great. Trina and I have Spanish together again in Mrs. Swenson's class and we're partnering up in Ms. Phillips' English class to do a book report. Amy and I are partners again in badminton, but she mentioned she might be moving at the end of the school year."

Mama cut up the brisket. She was getting comfortable in the kitchen. The tutorial with Chef Tuan paid off. "Where is Amy moving to?"

"Back to Hong Kong," I said sadly. "Why can't people just stay in one place? I miss my friends in Seattle, especially Marina, and now I might lose Amy to Hong Kong!"

Mama sliced the onions and placed slivers behind her ears. "This is the trick to not crying when you cut them." Two minutes later, she sniffled and wiped her eyes with the back of her hand. "Maybe I am too close." She slid a step stool under her feet and then stood a foot higher.

I laughed at her. "Mama, I don't think that's the secret." I ran to my room and came back with sunglasses and Ace's bandana tied around the bottom half of my face. I slipped my hands through two plastic produce bags. "This is how you cut onions."

Mama placed her onion slices over my ears. "Extra safe."

I looked ridiculous but humored her for a while as we talked about school. "Van is not doing good in her classes. She doesn't understand things like I do."

"It is good you are helping her." Mama tossed me the parsley. "Chop these."

"Are you making *bò kho*?" I loved Vietnamese beef stew with sweet potatoes and French baguettes.

"No," Mama said. She scrubbed the mushrooms, and my curiosity peaked. "I am making a French dish. It is beef bougie ngon."

"Oh," I said. "You mean like a beef bouillon?"

"What booyon? I said bougie, like a bourgeois." She repeated "bougie ngon" louder, as if saying it again at a higher decibel would make me understand.

"Okay, Mama, I get it," I said. "I'm not deaf. You're making a fancy beef dish that is delicious. Ngon means delicious. I get it."

Mama shook her head. "Ói zòi oi! Trời đất ơi!" *Oh my God! Heaven and Earth!* She took out the spiral-bound journal that Chef Tuan gave her.

Inside the pages were hand-written recipes. She flipped to page nineteen. Emphatically, she pointed at the recipe.

I read it out loud. "Boeuf Bourguignon."

"That's what I said."

At the end of that week, the Friday of spring break, Ace and I hung out in my room and did our usual thing while my mama and stepdad were at the Asian Garden Mall. Binh worked at the store selling ceramics while Mama studied for her citizenship exam in the back office.

"What time will they be home?" Ace asked. "We can go to the beach, and I'll have you back in plenty of time. They won't know you were gone."

I frowned. "I have to do some weeding, clean up the kitchen, and cook a pot of rice."

"I'll help you." He turned on the audiovisual system. "Wow, you have the latest episode of *Paris by Night!*" He popped in the VHS tape. "Thúy Nga Productions, video eighteen, season six."

My parents, like most Vietnamese families, had stacks of these *Paris by Night* videotapes. Each series was a variety show. Ace loved the slapstick comedy skits and Vietnamese folk songs called *cải lương*. I never appreciated these folk opera songs because they sounded so nasally and melodramatic. The comedy skits were over my head, and I didn't understand most of the humor. I enjoyed the performances of the pop and new wave singers who wore glitzy clothes and danced to choreographed movements with their sexy backup dancers.

Every time Lynda Trang Dai performed, I dropped everything and pretended I was her. Lynda was controversial because she wore skin-tight, lacy clothes and drank beer from a bottle. She sang in Vietnamese and English and was considered the Vietnamese Madonna. Others emulated her, but I considered them copycats of the OG, original gangster, of the new wave scene.

My mama had her favorite singers as well, like Huong Lan and Khanh Ha. Oddly enough, my stepdad liked Tuan Anh, who reminded me of Prince, Boy George, and Elton John all rolled into one with his outlandish style. His clothes were flashy, his shoes stilettoed or platformed, his hair a beehive mullet, and his face a bit odd with a mustache over heavy makeup. There was no denying it, however, he had solid vocals and was a talented artist.

Ace cooked the rice while I tidied up the kitchen. He washed the dishes and I arranged them neatly in the dishwasher to dry. We took a quick nibble break. Ace made us some condensed milk toast, which I had never had, but it was nirvana at first bite. Whereas Americans like their peanut butter and jelly sandwiches, the Vietnamese like their condensed milk and butter sandwiches, toasted, and enjoyed warm with strong jasmine or green tea. It gave us the little pep we needed to tackle the weeds together. After an hour in the hot sun, sweat poured down our face and our shoulders drooped.

"I need to shower," Ace said. "Want to join me?"

We had never seen each other naked before. I hesitated and cracked my neck. I inhaled deeply and smiled but did not advance toward him. The thought of seeing him bare-skinned and feeling the water cascade down our bodies excited me. My mouth was dry. I opened the fridge and grabbed a Mountain Dew. The brave and impulsive side of me was ready to make the leap for adventure and take our relationship to the next level. The innocent and apprehensive side of me was concerned the mystery and sexual tension between us would dissolve if I saw all of him.

"You shower first," I said. "Make it quick."

Ace laughed. He hopped into the shower while I put the weeds in the trash bin. I came back to the house and caught him by surprise, bare-chested and in his boxer briefs. My face flushed and I licked my lips. I looked past his shoulder to the imaginary poster behind him.

Ace tried to make me laugh and gyrated his hips. "Look at me. I'm an American gigolo."

I giggled. "Oh boy, Richard Gere, the American gigolo, in my home!"

Ace swaggered over to me and closed the distance between us. He caressed my cheek and bent down to find my parted lips. His skin felt like silk, and his body radiated so much heat that I wanted to take my shirt off to cool down. He carried me to my room and gently laid me down. The weight of his body on mine was comforting, and the more he rubbed his hips against mine, the more I wanted to open myself up and invite him in.

His warm breath in my ear sent tingles down to my toes. "You have to say 'stop' or else I won't be able to."

I felt his hardness against my thigh and his soft lips on my clavicle. "More." I arched my back and offered myself to him. "Don't stop."

Torn between passion and responsibility, we lay there kissing and exploring each other, touching every curve, every fold, every inch. His thumb caressed the raised part of my scar from my open-heart surgery and I guided his hand away from my scar. I held my breath. It was the one part of me that made me feel ugly, insecure, and unworthy of affection. I stopped kissing him and tried to sit up.

Ace stopped and looked at me. "That's the part I find the most beautiful." He lifted my shirt and kissed my surgical scar, all six inches of it from the top of my collarbone down to the end. "You're a warrior. It's your battle scar, and you cheated death."

I hugged him close and wrapped my legs around him. "How did I get so lucky?"

Two car doors slammed shut. Footsteps tapped the pavement. Keys jingled. Shit. Voices. I heard my parents. We had lost track of time. Thankfully, Ace's Supra was parked outside on the street in front of the nearby apartment complex. Ace scrambled to put his pants on but did not have time to get his shirt on. Heavy footsteps approached my bedroom. I threw the blanket over Ace and had him lie as flat and still as possible. My heart raced, and I crossed my hands involuntarily over my chest to keep my heart from bulleting through. The door opened. I froze. My stepdad popped his head in. He looked at me then closed my door.

"You better come here," Binh said. "Your daughter is hiding a boy in her room."

8. THE GOODBYE (SPRING 1990)

I stormed out of my room before Binh and my mama could come in. I was furious that my stepdad had barged into my room without knocking and without permission.

"You can't knock?" I screamed. "What if I were naked? I need privacy!"

My stepdad pounded his fist on the dinner table. "Not in my house you don't! Your door is to always remain open and unlocked. You cannot be trusted."

Mama sat down and bowed her head in shame. Wetness glistened around her eyes as she blinked to hold them back. "Is it true?" Disappointment and shame were written all over her face.

"Nothing happened," I argued.

"Then why was he in your room and your bed?" My stepdad was so angry he kicked Nikki. She flew across the rug and skidded on the kitchen floor. She yelped, and I ran to check on her.

Ace stepped into the room and bowed to my parents. "Please forgive—"

"Who the hell are you?" My stepdad said coldly. "What do you have to say for yourself, young man? Do you know she is only fifteen?"

"I love your daughter," Ace said. "I know she is young but—"

"Did you touch my daughter?" Mama asked.

"I am calling the police," Binh said.

"No!" I ran and stood next to Ace, holding a trembling Nikki in my arms. I hugged her close and patted her head. I was so pissed off that I lost my temper. "I fucking despise you. You're nothing but a demon." I grabbed the vase on the table and threw it at his feet.

"Do you see how she is talking to me?" Binh asked. "Control your daughter. She is a disrespectful little whore."

"She is anything but—" Ace didn't have the chance to finish.

My stepdad punched him in the jaw. "Shut up. You do not get to talk."

Tears ran down my mama's face. "Please, stop fighting. I'm tired of the two of you with this power struggle you have with one another. I just want peace for once in my life!"

My stepdad pointed at the door. "Young man, get out while you can. See what you made her do?"

Ace bowed deeply to my mama. "I am sorry. Please forgive me." He gave me an apologetic nod and headed to the door. I grabbed his wrist. "No, Christine, you stay here and make peace with them. I will see you later."

"No, you will not," my stepdad said. He escorted Ace to the door and slammed it shut. "While you live at my house—"

"It's not your house," I argued. "Mama lives here too. Or is she just another one of your possessions, like your car and your business and your garden? Everything is fucking yours. I thought marriage was a partnership. It should be 'ours,' not 'mine.'"

My stepdad bent down slowly and picked the vase off the floor. He placed it back on the table. It was eerie how methodical and calculated his movements were and how he suddenly was quiet. Was he premeditating my murder? Was he devising a plan to get rid of me? I braced myself for an explosion. I was ready to run if he threw the vase at me or put his hands on me.

My mama sat there and cried. She did not stand up to him. She did not defend me. She could not even look at me. I dishonored her. My beautiful, strong, gentle mother sat immobile. Was she frozen in fear? I wasn't going to live my life in fear. I wasn't going to let a man rob me of my spirit. I vowed I would never depend on a man for money or security.

I ran out the front door and looked for Ace, hoping to see his car still parked on the street. It was. I rapped frantically on the window and vaulted in the car with Nikki tucked close to my chest. Ace drove around aimlessly. We sat in silence. What now? I knew I could not go back, and somehow I needed to wake Mama up and convince her to leave him. Her life was too entwined with his. It was not going to be easy. He controlled everything and managed the finances…or should I say, mismanaged? He spent lavishly and liked to show off. He gave our products away freely to flatter people. In turn, they saw him as kind and generous and praised him as a shrewd businessman who had it all. He had a beautiful wife, a straight-A daughter, and a successful business.

I hated being Vietnamese then. Our society was built upon the stupid, patriarchal, male-chauvinistic belief that the man was in charge. A man could do no wrong and was the stronger of the two sexes. A woman's role was to be obedient, subservient, and cater to her husband. A child's job was to do, not think, and act, not speak. I denounced my ethnicity, my Vietnamese name, my language, and everything that was associated with the culture. In feeling that way, I also inadvertently denounced everything that Mama represented…everything that she was…and I hurt her more than I understood. Was I being insolent, selfish, and irresponsible? Was I insensitive?

###

I begged Ace to let me stay with him, but he insisted I go home. He lived with his two roommates and was not comfortable with me being there alone when he was at work. I couldn't live with Van. Her parents were dealing with personal issues at the time and could barely afford to pay the rent or feed themselves. I couldn't live with Amy and her sister, Mina. They were packing up to move to Hong Kong. Ace and I argued that night. It was our first fight, and I couldn't convince him to let me live with him. Why did he have to be so righteous?

Ace dropped me back off at home. "You have to swallow your pride and make up with your stepdad. If it were my daughter, I would be upset too, but they love you."

"He doesn't love me," I said.

"Well, your mom loves you, and she needs you." He kissed me, gave me some money in case I needed anything for the weekend, then drove away.

I quietly opened the door to the house and let Nikki inside. I tiptoed to my room, grabbed a thick sweatshirt, my purse, and slipped back into the night. Through Sigler Park and to the Catholic church I walked, engrossed in my self-pity and sadness. I wanted to disappear. I didn't care what happened to me. I wished someone would jump me and stab me to death. I let my imagination go dark and thought about finding Mad Dog, Jade, Juice, and the rest of the Pomona Boys.

I walked in a daze, entranced in a make-believe world where it was just Ace and me, living happy and stuck in time. Inside the church, a light was on. The glow illuminated the face of the Blessed Virgin Mary on the stained glass windows. I curled my fingers around the door handle and pulled, only to discover it was locked. I walked to the side and back entrances, but those doors were locked as well. I knocked and waited, but nobody came.

I felt so alone. I was alone. I huddled behind the dumpster and slumped to the ground. A whimper became a demonic cry, and I released my troubled spirit into the night. Exhausted, I curled into a ball with my back against the unforgiving wall, and with one last sigh escaping my lips, I slept.

Saturday, I walked five miles to Van's house. The moment she opened the door, tears sprang from my eyes. I sobbed and told her the whole story.

"Go take a bath," Van said. "I'll get you some fresh clothes. You stink."

I didn't tell her I slept behind a dumpster. I ran a hot bubble bath and soaked in the soothing water. I didn't know how I was going to recover from this. Seeing Ace again would be forbidden. Existing without him in my life, without seeing him each day, was a death sentence.

Moving to California had been a big mistake. I had to find a way to return to Seattle. I sat numb and devoid of feelings. The world around me didn't matter anymore. Maybe everyone would be better without me. I didn't have anything to contribute. Ace would find another girlfriend eventually. He would soon tire of me and want a real woman.

What did I have to offer? I wasn't Vietnamese enough. I wasn't American enough. I wasn't smart enough, pretty enough, or talented enough. Was there anything worse than being ordinary? I got out of the tub and looked for a razor blade or something sharp. Girls slit their wrists every day. People committed suicide all the time. Mama didn't have to feel stuck in the middle anymore. I dragged her down, not Binh. She finally found love, and I ruined it for her. All these years, I was the rope around her wrists and the burden on her back. When she stumbled and fell, I wasn't there to catch her. When she needed to fly, I tethered her to the boulder. No more. *I'll set you free, Mama. I'll set both of us free.*

I found a shaving kit below the sink and took the razor out. Would it be sharp enough? I could try. I scraped the blades against my wrist. I didn't feel anything. Harder. You have to press harder. I dug the teeth deeper into my skin. Crisscross, like a tic tac toe. Again. Harder. Deeper.

At last, I drew blood and watched it drip. Fascinated, I sat back in the tub and zombied out. The haze of blood clouded the water and turned it a subdued red. I leaned back and closed my eyes. Everything would be okay.

Ace's face hovered inches from mine. The scent of his cologne carried me to a tropical island, and I ran along the shore. The sun beat down on me. I sat up but was pulled back by arms I recognized.

Ace's voice was soothing. "Close your eyes." I did as I was told. "I've got you, honey."

I smiled. I was in heaven. We were together.

"She's awake?"

Wait, why was Van in heaven too? I opened my eyes. Posters of Brett Michaels, Sebastian Bach, and Vince Neil hung on the walls. A large cross loomed above the headboard. I was in Van's bedroom and leaning against Ace's chest. My voice cracked when I spoke. "What happened?"

Van sat on the corner of the bed and squeezed my foot. "I called him." She nodded at Ace. "He came right away. I think you tried to kill yourself."

"You didn't call the ambulance?" I asked.

"No," Van said, "because you just fell asleep, that's all."

"You mean, I failed?" I didn't understand. I thought I was dying. "But I cut myself, and I was bleeding. I felt my life force and all the energy drain away."

"Honey," Ace said, "you had just walked five miles to get here. I'm sure you didn't sleep well last night either. I know I didn't." Ace handed me a can of cold *sữa đậu nành*. The sweetened soy milk tasted like the fountain of youth and rejuvenated me.

"What now?" I asked. "I don't want to go back home."

"I wish you could stay here with us, but—"

"It's okay, Van," I said. "I know things are tough with your dad losing his job. Maybe I can ask Trina and her mom. In three months, school will be out, and maybe things will be better."

"In the meantime," Ace said, "I'm getting you a beeper." Ace unclipped his beeper off his belt loop and showed it to me. "You can call my pager and punch in the number you're at. If it's an emergency just put 9-1-1 after it, and I'll call you back. And if it's not urgent or you just want to send me a message that you love me, put in 8-0-0-8."

Van laughed and slapped Ace on the shin. "Oh my God."

"Why 8-0-0-8?" I asked.

"My dumbass cousin wants you to spell 'BOOB.'"

I punched Ace playfully and gave him a charley horse. He feigned injury by hobbling out of bed and limping to the living room.

I called Trina that afternoon and asked if she'd talk to her mom about me staying with them for three months until school was out. I explained the situation at home but left out the part about having a boyfriend five years older than I was. We did not have to beg for Trina's mom, Auntie Chanh, to accept my request. They wanted me out of that volatile situation and believed I needed to feel safe and untroubled to finish the school year strong.

We agreed that on Monday after school, Trina would walk home with me to my house and help me gather my things. Trina's mom would pick us up and take us home.

I stayed with Van for the weekend and called home once to tell Mama I was safe. She was worried out of her mind and demanded I come home. I stood my ground and told her I'd be home Monday after school to collect my things.

###

My dear friend, Trina, sat on my bed and petted Nikki. It broke my heart to leave my dog behind, but I convinced myself it was temporary. Mama swore she would take good care of my pup. In the corner of the room was my duffle bag stuffed with my badminton rackets, team competition clothes, and birdies. Next to it was a trash bag of shoes and ten outfits to last me until laundry day. I wanted to be all packed before Mama got home. She was studying hard for her citizenship exam, and I urged her to take the time she needed. I promised I'd stay until she got home.

"I feel like I'm forgetting something," I said.

"Pajamas?" Trina asked.

"Got 'em. I've got underwear, bras, a jacket..."

"Toothbrush? Makeup?"

"Oh, yeah, I need my toothbrush and hairbrush."

After I finished, we sat and waited. Trina was an amazing friend. She was my cheerleader, always encouraging and supportive. She was not only studious but smart. I knew she'd be a doctor, lawyer, or engineer one day, which was what every Vietnamese family seemed to want for their children. My dearest friend was most comfortable when she was outside of the spotlight, behind the scenes, where it was safe and predictable. She had a pure heart. I teased her for her shyness and tried to bring her out of her shell. She carried a little extra weight, and I guess that affected her confidence. She was soft-spoken with the cutest, childish laugh. When she was happy, her dimples came out in full glory, and I envied her dimples. The Vietnamese have a superstition about dimples being signs of good fortune and luck. In some ways, she was lucky. She had a mother who loved her whole-heartedly and protected her fiercely. Sadly, her mom couldn't protect her from everything or everyone. Her father had molested her, and that perhaps explained why she often turned away from the limelight, preferring to recoil inward rather than shine outward.

"Is your stepdad really an ass?" Trina asked. "I mean, he always seems so nice and gracious."

I was flabbergasted. "Don't play devil's advocate, Trina. I can't believe you just asked me that. You're usually on my side."

"I guess I don't know him as you do," she said.

"No, you don't." I debated whether to confess and tell her about Ace. Since our conversation went dry, I spilled the beans and told her everything.

"That explains why you hadn't been boy crazy over Julio!" Trina straightened her back and sat up taller. "I thought maybe you were seeing my neighbor, Tommy. He has a crush on you."

"What?" I put my hands to my cheeks and sat back against the wall. "Tommy? Tall, skinny 'I'm a slut' Tommy?"

We both laughed. Tommy was a flirt and always chased skirts. He thought of himself as a lady's man and made his move on anyone desperate enough for attention.

"He put his arm around me once, and I smacked him," Trina said.

"Good for you," I said. "He'd be a lot cuter if he plucked that caterpillar stache growing above his lips."

"Agreed," Trina said. "So…have you and Ace done it?"

"You mean had sex?" I asked.

"No." Trina rolled her eyes. "Study for the SATs. Of course, I mean sex. After all, it's unrealistic that you'd be a virgin for that long."

She was right. When we were together, we couldn't stop touching each other. It was always he who pulled away before we crossed the boundaries. How long would he be able to stay level-headed and in control?

Mama came home before I could confirm or deny. We came out of the bedroom and greeted her. She looked ten years older, haggard and disheveled in her appearance. I noticed she had two different colored socks on but didn't say anything. Dark smudges smeared her eyes, which drooped in solidarity with her mouth and cheeks. Her tanned skin no longer looked vibrant and youthful. Rather, the brown tinge showcased her age and the weathered expression on her face. Sadness sucker punched me in the gut, and guilt swallowed me whole.

Mama and I stood in the kitchen and talked while Trina waited in my room with Nikki. I let Mama start as I didn't know what to say.

Her eyes misted. "Thủy-Tiên ơi…Do you know how broken my heart is?" I shook my head and the tears I had held back quietly fell down my cheeks. Mama clutched her heart. "You tell me what to do. I want you to be happy, but I need to be happy too. You are growing up so fast, and you do not need your old mother like you used to."

I shook my head. "That is not true. I need you, truly I do, more than anything."

Mama patted my head and stroked my hair. "My entire life has been devoted to you, and I know it has always been just the two of us."

I knelt and grabbed her hand. I pressed her soft hands to my forehead, hands that once held me and fed me, hands that were once smooth and youthful but now wrinkled and spotted from cooking oil burns, and I begged for forgiveness.

"I'm sorry, Mama," I whispered. "I don't mean to be a bad daughter." It was hard to breathe. My nose was stuffy, and the more I sniffed, the harder I cried. I was such a disappointment. I knew this. Selfish, stupid, angry. And for what reason? Why did I feel so threatened by my stepdad, by this authority?

"For once," Mama said, "I am ashamed of you, but I cannot blame you. It is my fault for loving you and spoiling you too much, for holding on too tightly, because I was always afraid of losing you."

I wrapped my arms around her knees and pressed my head against her leg. "I'll do better. I'll try harder. I don't want to make you sad."

I lowered myself to the floor, still on my knees, and grabbed her ankles. I kissed Mama's feet. "I know I hurt you. I know I am an unworthy, ungrateful daughter. Please, forgive me. Please still love me. Don't give up on me. Please." The tears flowed. I hated myself. My bones ached and sorrow crushed my rib cage. I had no heart, no soul, to keep it from caving in.

Mama lowered herself to my level and sat on the floor with me. She wept. She cradled me in her arms and rocked me like a baby. I clung to her, but no matter how tightly I held onto her or how much I crushed her, desperately trying to be one with her, I could not get close enough. It left me drained, unfulfilled and wanting to disappear into her arms.

"Maybe this break will be good for us," Mama said. "It is only for three months. Miss Chánh is kind to take you in, and Trina is a good girl. Promise me you will not give them any trouble. Be respectful and dutiful, help around the house, do your schoolwork."

"Yes, Mama, I promise," I said. "Are you going to be all right?"

Mama lifted my chin. She kissed my forehead. "I will be all right for you if you be all right for me."

"And what about my boyfriend?" I asked. "His name is Ace. He loves me, and I love him."

"I know I cannot keep the two of you apart," Mama said. "Your stepdad and I will invite him over, and we will talk to him to understand his intentions."

"You will see," I said. "He is good." We sat in silence for a few minutes, respectful of each other's thoughts. "Mama, how is your studying going?"

"By August, I should be a naturalized citizen," Mama said, "and so will you."

That was news to me. "Do I have to take a test?"

"No, since you are under eighteen, you automatically become a citizen when I become one."

"Does this mean I can change my name and be legally any name I want?" I asked. Mama nodded. "Are you going to change your name?"

"I always liked Elizabeth Taylor, so I am thinking of changing it to Liz."

"I think I will stick with Christine, but maybe spell it with a K."

Trina's mom, Auntie Chanh, arrived. While she and my mama exchanged cordial conversation, I stood back and observed. Trina looked nothing like her mother, who was thin and rather homely looking. They shared the same nose and were both soft-spoken, but whereas Auntie Chanh had short, wavy locks, Trina had a long, straight mane with bangs that reached for the sky like vines held up by excessive Aqua Net hairspray.

I collect my bags, hugged Mama, and slowly walked away, determined not to cry. It was another difficult goodbye but far from my last. A few more farewells were to come.

*

9. TICKING TIME BOMB (SPRING-SUMMER 1990)

Sophomore life resumed as usual at Westminster High School, but now I laid my head at Trina's house instead of my mama's. The day I said goodbye to Amy and her sister Mina was the day I decided to change my name to Amy. What better way to celebrate our friendship and to honor the girl who had a profound impact on me in the short amount of time she was in my life? I was evolving away from the reckless Christine to a more aware and cosmopolitan Amy. She was everything I envisioned myself to be. She was well-traveled, athletic, funny, smart, and fashionable. She was respectful, outgoing, and accepting of everyone. She was competitive, but humble and gracious, and carried optimism around her shoulders like a warm shawl no matter the situation. In a few months, Mama and I would become citizens of the US and change our names to Liz and Amy.

I spent the Saturday before Mina and Amy left for Hong Kong with them and a couple of friends from school in Little Saigon. We shopped for trinkets, took silly pictures, and ate our way up and down Bolsa Avenue. We were teenagers on the loose, and it was a blast until we got to the Asian Garden Mall. I stopped in to say hello to my mama, but as I rode up the escalator and saw Ace's face come into view, my body stiffened. What were they talking about? How long had he been there? Why hadn't he told me he was meeting my parents at the shop? I remained calm. *It's good they're having an open dialogue.*

They abruptly stopped talking when they saw me with my friends. I stood next to Ace and slipped my hand into his. My stepdad's face grew stern, but he didn't say anything. I introduced my friends and told them to wait for me at the food court downstairs.

Ace was composed, respectful, and articulate when he spoke. "Your daughter's education is important to me. I would not stand in her way from graduating high school and going on to college."

"And how will you support her?" Mama asked.

I squeezed Ace's hand. "He's going to be an engineer, Mama."

"Yes." Ace squeezed my hand back. "I am a software engineer apprentice at IBM, but I want to go into sales."

"There is good money in sales." I looked at my stepdad for an approving nod, thinking he would appreciate and understand the world of sales. Instead, he looked at his fingernails and picked his nose.

"Right now I work with a team of developers and am learning software design, testing, and computing," Ace said.

My stepdad crossed his arms over his chest and leaned back in his chair. "Sales requires traveling. How are you going to protect her if you're gone for days or weeks at a time?"

Ace did not flinch or hesitate. "I don't have to travel domestically or internationally. I could stay local until Christine and I are ready for me to be more global. With all due respect, this will not happen overnight, so we have time to figure out the details of our future together."

"Let me remind you also that she is still a minor, and if you take her innocence away, I will be the first to visit you in jail and personally watch you rot in there." My stepdad's words were harsh.

Mama frowned, and my body temperature rose. I was ready to tell him exactly what I thought about his interrogation and threats.

Ace squeezed my hand tighter, and the veins in his neck stood out, but he remained collected. He took the high road and did not give my stepdad any ammunition. Ace nodded. "Understood."

"Then we agree," Mama said. "And since we are allowing you two to continue dating, maybe you should move back home." Mama looked at me while keeping one eye on Binh's reaction.

"Auntie Chanh has been very good to me," I said, "and I wouldn't feel right changing my mind back and forth. She went to great trouble to accommodate me with a bed and personal space for my things."

"It is better this way," Binh said, "because we have news to share."

I looked from him to Mama for answers. She smiled and looked thrilled.

"We are buying a house," Mama said. "We will be moving out of the rental house."

The news saddened me. I enjoyed being neighbors with Leena and Loanne. Although I did not see them often, it was comforting to know they were next door and could pop in anytime.

"Where is the new house?" I asked.

"Huntington Beach," Mama said excitedly. "By the time we get settled in, school will be out, and you can move back home. We will have a fresh start as a family."

I was not happy about moving to Huntington Beach. This meant a new school in a different district. I would be far from Trina and Van. Knowing that my days at Westminster High were numbered, I immediately went sour. My expression changed from hopeful to pessimistic. This annoyed my stepdad.

"This isn't about you," he said, "and you can't have everything you want in life."

"I know that," I said sarcastically. "I'm just absorbing the news. Can't you give me that basic right to have emotions and opinions?"

Now I had done it. He was angry. "I think we are done here. Go join your friends."

I hugged my mama and walked out with Ace, but before exiting, I glanced back and fired a disgruntled glare at Binh. I could not harness my emotions or swallow my tongue as Ace did. Not to speak my mind was to admit defeat. I did not want to pick my battles with my stepdad. I wanted to win every one of them. I knew I was starting a war, but I didn't care. I was confident I would win because, in the end, Mama always had my back. She always picked me. I was too strong-willed and would not bend so long as he continued to talk to me in a demeaning manner as if I were subhuman.

We joined my friends at the food court, and it took little convincing to let go of the grudge. The rest of the afternoon was about Amy and Mina. Ace bought us desserts, and we walked to a nearby park to throw a frisbee. We had so much fun I did not want the joy to end. By seven o'clock we were back in front of the mall. Amy and Mina's mom waited there to take them home. The three of us hugged and cried. We promised to write and send pictures. Saying goodbye to them was like saying goodbye to Marina, Jen, Melissa, and all my Seattle friends again.

I told Amy that by the time I started eleventh grade, I would be a citizen and my legal name would be Amy Le. Before they drove off, I said my farewell by quoting Anne Shirley from *Anne of Green Gables*, saying we'd be strangers living side by side. And with that, the other half of me departed to live her life in Hong Kong.

A few weeks after Amy and Mina moved, I walked to Mama's house after school to see how the packing was going. I was excited to see my dog, Nikki, and wanted to retrieve my diary from under my bed. I needed to collect a few things to carry me over until school let out for the summer. We were uprooting as a family and moving to Huntington Beach where I would start my junior year at Ocean View High School.

"I'm here," I called out. No answer. The door was unlocked, but neither Binh nor my mom was home. Perhaps they were next door visiting with Leena and Loanne's parents. "Nikki, where are you, little girl?" I walked into my room expecting to see my Chihuahua nestled on her doggie bed sleeping or wagging her tail. "Nikki?" She wasn't there and neither was her bed or toys.

I opened my closet, ran down the hall, looked in the bathrooms, and checked my parents' bedroom, but she was gone. Panic-stricken, I ran to the living room and out the back door to the yard and garden. She was nowhere in sight. Back in the kitchen, I opened the cupboard. Her dog food was not there. There was no trace of Nikki.

"What the hell did you do?" I said out loud. My thoughts immediately blamed my stepdad for her disappearance. My mind raced in circles. I was worried sick. My stomach rolled. My lunch crept up my throat but I suppressed it with a hard swallow. I sat down to calm myself but stood again, too agitated and restless. I couldn't wait for Binh to walk through the front door. I was firing on all cylinders and ready to harm him if he had given Nikki away or hurt her in some way.

I tramped to my room, huffing and grunting in anger, to get my Candies shoes, a pair of Jordache jeans, and my bomber jacket. I stuffed them into my badminton duffle bag. I lifted my mattress to get my diary, but it was not there. I lifted each corner of the mattress, but my journal had vanished. Had he found it? Had he read it? Oh, this was not good.

I sat on the couch in the living room, ready to confront him. The door swung open, and my stepdad walked in holding hands with a lady who was not my mom. They immediately let go when they saw me. I grew suspicious. The woman had features like my mom except she was taller, wore glasses, and had surgery on her eyelids to make them double-lidded. I could tell her eyes used to be monolidded by the puffiness around them and the bruising above the incision. I saw no reason to be cordial. I curtly asked about Nikki.

"Your dog was a nuisance," he said flatly. "I gave her away."

"What?" I yelled. "When? To whom?" I could not believe Mama let that happen.

"She is with a good family. Don't worry. It was too much to take care of her."

"You couldn't take care of a little five-pound dog?" I asked sarcastically. "That's a bunch of bullshit. You're an asshole. You've taken everything I love away from me. You're punishing me because I am not some docile girl you can control and bully. Do I scare you? Am I a competition?"

"Shut up!" he screamed. "I've had enough of your mouth."

"Where is my diary, huh?" I clenched my teeth and looked around for something to throw at him. We both reached for the heavy phone book on the table. I was faster and held it above my head, ready to chuck it at him as hard as I could. This time I was not aiming at his feet.

"Go ahead." He dared me and egged me on. "Know this though. You throw that at me, and I will make sure you end up in a wheelchair for the rest of your life. I will hunt you down and shoot you, not to kill you, no, to make sure you never live a meaningful life again. You will rot in that wheelchair, and your boyfriend can wipe the shit from your mouth and the drool from your ass."

I lowered the phone book. I believed his vile threat. "You do that, and you'll lose my mama forever."

"She is already slipping away from me because of you," he said coldly.

"You're a son of a bitch."

"How dare you insult my mother." Binh advanced in one swift stride and grabbed hold of the book. I gripped tighter with both hands and pulled as hard as I could. We tugged until I let go, and he stumbled back.

"You're a cheating bastard." I glanced at the woman he brought home. She stood horrified and speechless. "He's not worth it."

I ran for the door but was jerked back with tremendous force. Binh's lady friend gasped. I fell flat on my butt and a sharp pain shot up my spine. I winced and cried out. The woman tried to help me up, but I brushed her hand away.

"One way or another, I am getting rid of you," Binh said. "I read your diary and all the foul things you called me. If your mom knew what kind of child she raised and all your secrets, she'd send herself to the grave."

"First of all, do you think you have that much power over her that she'd kill herself because of you?" I laughed. "And you want to talk about secrets? Does Mama know about your porn magazines and tapes? Does she know you're sneaking behind her back? You're despicable."

"Get out!" Binh screamed, and both his friend and I flinched. His body shook, and he stormed to his room. I knew my stepdad had guns and rifles in the house. I ran out of the house as fast as I could and did not look back. I ran to the church and asked if I could make a phone call. I paged Ace with a 9-1-1 at the end. He called me back in under five minutes, but it felt like an eternity before the phone rang.

In twenty minutes, the Supra pulled up, and I threw myself into Ace's arms. I bawled and vomited the whole story. I begged Ace again to reconsider letting me live with him. I suggested he move out and find a cheaper place to live. I offered to get a job and help with utilities. My pleading fell on deaf ears, and this sparked another argument. I knew I was in a fragile and desperate state, but I didn't see any other options.

"Maybe Trina's mom will let you stay for another year so you can go to Westminster High for your junior year."

I nodded. "Do you think Auntie Chanh will agree? I can find an after-school job and help out."

"I can pitch in, too, to help with food," Ace said.

The world looked a little better with the possibility of me living at Trina's house. I held Ace tightly and showered him with kisses. "I guess you can't have a rainbow without the rain."

"You can't have a rainbow without the sun either." Ace kissed me tenderly. "There will be a lot of rainbows in your future, babe."

Mama was adamant I come home and not burden Auntie Chanh for another year. "Absolutely not. We agreed on three months until the end of the school year." She didn't understand how much I loathed my stepdad. I found it impossible to be in his presence. How would I tell Mama about the things I knew and the things he said? Would it make a difference? Surely it had to.

"Fine, I'll come home, but there are things you need to know."

I moved back in with my parents to our new Huntington Beach home. I expected a lovely home near the beach but was surprised when we rolled up to the gates of a mobile home park for residents fifty-five years old and above. Senior housing? Really? I would be living in a double-wide with the senior community? Mama was fifty-one, so Binh had to be fifty-five or older. I was ready to turn around and walk back out the gate.

In the first month, my interactions with Binh were minimal. We avoided each other like a virus and spoke only when necessary. Mama either didn't notice or pretended not to notice the strain between her husband and her daughter.

Ace and I saw each other less and less as his job with IBM became more involved. I resumed my summer VSL schooling at the church with other teenagers and improved on my language skills, mastering the accents and pronunciations of the Vietnamese words but still not understanding everything when they were strung together. I took a job helping the residents around the mobile park, doing light yard work, weeding, trimming, planting, and digging dirt. It didn't pay much, and my job was not steady, but it afforded me a little financial independence. Sometimes they tipped me with fresh baked cookies or extra servings of chili. Sometimes I worked for free just to get out of the house.

For my sixteenth birthday, my parents surprised me with a birthday party. I was allowed to invite one friend. It was a toss between inviting Van or Ace, but Ace decided for me.

"I have separate plans for us," Ace said. "You spend it with Van, and we will celebrate your birthday the following week."

"Not much of a party when it's just me and Van," I murmured.

"Cheer up," Ace said. "You also have your mom and stepdad."

I punched him. "Haha. Not funny."

We picked Van up from her house and drove north out of Westminster. The locale was kept hush-hush, so Van and I were excited.

"Do you think we're going to Six Flags Magic Mountain?" Van whispered.

"Maybe," I said, "but that's kind of far. Maybe Disneyland."

"Or Knott's Berry Farm," Van said. "I want to ride the Bigfoot Rapids."

"We are almost there," Binh said.

Van and I looked out the window, confused. Nothing but strip malls and car dealerships surrounded us.

"Maybe it's at a restaurant?" I asked Van. She shrugged.

We pulled into a large parking lot, and the only business that stood out was the Chuck E. Cheese restaurant.

"You've got to be kidding me." I slumped in the car seat and banged my head against the leather.

Van tried to sound upbeat and joyful. "Oh, are we going to Chuck E. Cheese? I love their pizzas."

Mama smiled. "We knew you'd like it here. They have games and pizza—"

"And an animatronic band that's creepy," I said dryly.

Van elbowed me and shot me a warning look. "Hey, it's where a kid can be a kid."

"Yup," I said, "because I'm still a kid."

"I think you will have fun," Mama said. "Binh reserved a party table for you."

"Of course he did," I said.

"And you get game tokens and cake," Mama said.

"That's great," I responded. "How thoughtful." My tone was sarcastic, but only Van picked it up. My stepdad was ten feet ahead of us and kept his distance.

We made the best of the situation, and for my mama's sake, I pretended to have fun. The two hours dragged on, and by the time the cake came out, I wanted to sink into quicksand. I stumbled out of the pizza joint feeling like I had been in a spin cycle with obnoxious kids running around, spitting and spilling fluids everywhere, screaming over games and toys, and touching every surface with their sticky hands.

The following weekend, Ace planned an evening picnic for us at Huntington Beach. He got my parents' permission to keep me out until midnight and told them where we would be. I wore a new summer dress for the occasion and took extra time getting ready. Mama got me a new Caboodles cosmetic case filled with lip gloss, sparkly eye shadow, blush, and all the makeup and accessories a girl on the go would need.

We arrived at the beach forty-five minutes before sunset and laid our blanket on the warm sand. The soft breeze and salty air encouraged me to relax and enjoy the moment. I watched couples stroll the beach, hand in hand, laughing and talking with ease, and I wondered what brought them together.

Seagulls squawked overhead while kites fluttered in the wind. Nearby, a bonfire blazed, and the smell of burning wood put me at ease. I kicked off my shoes and knelt before the picnic basket.

Ace spread out an array of food he had picked up at a local deli. He bought egg rolls, *hom baos*, shrimp toast, meat pies called *paté số*, and my favorite, *bánh bèo*. These small, savory steamed rice cakes topped with mung beans, pork belly, toasted shrimp, fried scallions, and green onions were heaven in my mouth. The cakes were chewy while the meat provided some crunch. I loved soaking my bánh bèo in a lot of sweet chili fish sauce.

"I love street food," I exclaimed. "There is so much food though."

"And we have *bánh bông lan* for dessert," Ace said. "I figured a sponge cake would be less messy and can hold all the candles."

I laughed. "I'm sixteen, not sixty."

Ace chuckled. "I thought we'd celebrate our birthdays together. Mine is on August 15."

"Oh, that's less than two weeks away," I said.

He nodded. "So we need sixteen candles for you and twenty-one candles for me."

I looked at the sponge cake and shook my head. "I don't know, old man. I don't think this cake has room for all of your candles."

Ace pinned me to the blanket and stole a kiss. I felt his hardness against me and pushed him off before we lost ourselves in each other.

Ace sat up and cleared his throat. He poured cold water on his head and splashed a little on his crotch to cool down.

I laughed. "You peed your shorts."

He gave me a boyish grin. "Do you recognize this spot?"

I looked at the stretch of sand and the crashing waves and nodded. "This was where we went grunion running the first night we met after the Poison concert."

"That was over a year ago, and it was the night I fell in love with you," Ace said. "Your magic hit me hard. I felt it below the belt, and it ricocheted off my heart and into my gut. That was when I knew I belonged to you."

"You sure it wasn't the waves and the flippy floppy fish hitting you?" I teased.

"It probably was," he said with a smile, "but the moonlight disguised them as something more powerful, and it felt real."

We sat on the beach, ate our appetizers, and walked down nostalgia lane. We reminisced about the fun we had and daydreamed about the future. By nightfall, more bonfires were lit, and laughter drifted from every direction. Young lovers and best friends enjoyed one another's company, and West Coast hip hop music hit the beach scene. Ace and I danced and shared our food with a group of high schoolers. When it was time to blow out the candles on our cake, I wished that moment would last forever.

My wish did not come true. Two days after Ace's twenty-first birthday, my stepfather kicked me out of the house. My parents drove me seventy-five miles south of Huntington Beach and dumped me at a stranger's house.

My life unraveled, and overnight, my skin turned inside out. The agony of losing everything turned me into a ticking time bomb. No one was there to save me from exploding.

10. TWILIGHT ZONE (SUMMER 1990)

The following weekend after my beach birthday with Ace, Mama and I officially became naturalized citizens of the United States.

I proudly held my certificate of citizenship in my hand and read it out loud. "Be it known that Thuy Tien Ngoc Le, a.k.a. Amy Le, now residing at 6241 West Warner Avenue, Huntington Beach, California, having applied to the commissioner of Immigration and Naturalization for a certificate of citizenship pursuant to Section 341 of the Immigration and Nationality Act having proved to the satisfaction of the commissioner that she is now a citizen of the United States of America, became a citizen on August 10, 1990, and is now in the United States."

Gene McNary, the commissioner of the Immigration and Naturalization Service, signed it. I was proud of what Mama had accomplished. The path to citizenship had many requirements, including satisfactorily completing an interview, getting fingerprinted, undergoing a biometrics exam, and passing a civics test.

That evening we celebrated. I cut slabs of sirloin beef into bite-sized cubes while Mama prepared the vinaigrette. We made *bò lúc lắc*, a French-inspired beef cuisine shaken in a wok and served over a salad of lettuce, cucumbers, tomatoes, and onions.

"How do you say this word?" Mama took a brown bottle from the refrigerator. "Chef Tuấn gave this to me, but it has been used only once."

I shrugged my shoulders and sounded it out. "War...kester...sure? Worst...stir...shy...er. Hmm. I think it's wurster-sir." I put the Worcestershire sauce back in the fridge. "What do you use it for?"

"Chef Tuấn used the worsty-shir-shir thing on a steak." Mama stir-fried the beef and shook her butt while she shook the beef in the pan. "Beef shake shake."

She was so cute. I chuckled and shook my behind with her.

She flipped the meat over and shook both her butt and the pan. "Shake shake shake." She concentrated on shaking the meat lightly so that nothing flew out of the pan. When one of the pieces fell out, she picked the meat up with her chopsticks and threw it back in. It sizzled in protest. "Oh, still alive."

"Liz," I said.

Mama did not acknowledge me. I tested her name to see how it rolled off my tongue…tested to see if she knew her new name.

"Liz."

Nothing. She was in her zone, moving around the kitchen like a master chef. "Mama. Mom. Liz. Ma." I laughed. "Mẹ ơi!"

"What?" Mama froze. "Did I drop another piece?" She whirled around and looked on the floor.

I kissed her on the cheek. "Mama Liz, I am proud of you. You can cook and sew, and your English gets better year after year. Now you're a citizen. What is the next goal?"

Mama did not hesitate. "OMD. I want to practice acupuncture and be an Oriental medicine doctor."

"Oh, fancy," I exclaimed. "I guess someone has to be a doctor in the family. Ace is the engineer so I guess it's up to me to go into law. Do court reporters count?" I explained to Mama what a court reporter does and that there was a court reporting school not too far from where we lived. It sounded interesting to sit in courtrooms and record the proceedings.

"Typing is not lawyer work," Mama said. "You have to be a doctor, lawyer, or engineer."

Our conversation drifted to Ace and how things were going between us.

"We're behaving, Mama, I promise," I said. "Ace's birthday is on Wednesday. I'd like to do something special for him."

"Have him come over for dinner," Mama said.

"Can we not invite Binh?" I knew the answer…

Mama shook her head. "I thought you two were getting along better."

"We have a better understanding of each other now."

How could I tell her about the other woman? What would I say about his porn addiction? Where would I even begin? I didn't understand where all my anger stemmed from or how the distrust even began. Perhaps the genesis of my despair took root the night of my eighth-grade dance when he pulled me out of the gym and embarrassed me.

"Mama, why did you give my dog away? Brother Khoi and Linh gave Nikki to me as a gift and I can't believe you just gave her away without talking to me first."

"You were not home to take care of her, and both of us worked. It was not fair to leave her alone all the time. And she peed and pooped all over the house. She pooped in your stepdad's shoes, and he put his foot in it."

I laughed but caught myself. I gasped. No doubt my dog let him know in her not-so-subtle way what she thought of him. "Where is she now? Can I visit her?"

"Honestly, I do not know. Your stepdad had enough of her and gave her away the next day. I did not know until later that afternoon."

The lump in my throat settled in my chest and moved down to my stomach. Tears threatened to emerge, and I blinked them back.

Mama handed me four plates so I could set the table. "Four? Who is coming over?"

"A real estate friend of your stepdad's," Mama said. "Set the table and bring the pot of rice over."

"Are you lonely?" The question somersaulted out before I thought about it. "You don't have friends or family here. Brother Tree lives in San Jose and now that we live in Huntington Beach, you can't see our neighbors any time you want. You must miss Aunt Six and Uncle Seven terribly. And what about my dad? When was the last time you talked to him?"

"I have been too busy to think about it. Maybe this real estate friend of your stepdad's is nice and I can be friends with her."

I raised my eyebrows. "His friend is a woman?"

The door swung open with a creak, and my stepdad walked in. Our dinner guest stood behind him. The same two-lidded eyes, although no longer bruised and puffy, wearing the same glasses as last time. Her freshly permed and coiffed hair rose high above her forehead. She and I exchanged an uneasy glance. She lowered her eyes and looked away. I stared at her and pursed my lips. I mentally fired cannonballs at them. The audacity of this man. He had no shame.

"I don't feel well," I said. "I am going to lie down and rest and put some tiger balm ointment on my stomach."

"You are not going to eat?" Mama asked.

"Do not be rude," Binh said. "Say hello to Ms. Nga. You are going to join us for dinner. Your mom made all this nice food."

I mumbled a barely audible greeting, but no one pressed me to talk louder. Binh carried on as if he were entertaining royalty. He showed off his ceramics and bragged about his sales figures. He wrapped his arm around

Mama and pecked her on the cheek, raved about her culinary skills, and then praised me for my dedication to VSL school.

"Christine also got perfect grades last year," Binh said, "and she is great with a racket."

"My name is Amy now." I gritted my teeth. Would he never say it right?

We sat down to eat, and with the first bite of Mama's beef, Nga sank in her chair and closed her eyes. "Mmm." She complimented Mama on the tenderness of the shaken beef and tanginess of the salad. "I must get your recipe."

Mama blushed and put more food on Nga's plate. "Did you have eye surgery?"

Our guest nodded. She accepted extra portions of the food. "I need to put some fat on my body, like you."

I swallowed my spit and leaned in. Did she just insult my mama?

"Who wants to be skin and bones? It is a sign you are poor and starving. I'm jealous you have the extra weight. It stretches and smooths out the skin."

I rolled my eyes. Was this seriously happening? My stepdad sat there with this floozy and pretended it was a regular dinner among old friends. He showered Mama with affection and let his girlfriend spoon-feed Mama a multitude of insulting compliments. My stomach revolted, and I wanted to throw up. I imagined heaving and gurgling until cow diarrhea shot out of my mouth and all over Binh and Nga. I gripped my chopsticks tight and sat sullen, disengaged. The more Nga talked, the more Binh smacked his lips, and the more Mama dished food on their plates, the more I wanted to scream, pull my hair out, and flip the table upside down.

"Everyone in California is skinny," Mama said. "I know back in our country being plump was good, but I need to lose weight. Too much sitting and cooking." She laughed, but it sounded like a nervous, insecure laugh. It trailed off and abruptly ended.

"Christine—"

"It's Amy, Stepfather," I said coldly. "For the last freaking time. Say it with me. Amy."

My stepdad wiped his lips with his napkin and threw it emphatically on the table. He pushed his chair back and walked briskly to the bedroom.

Was he going to get his shotgun? I told myself to run, but my legs would not move.

Mama and Nga looked at each other. Fear, concern, and curiosity marred their faces. The three of us waited silently for his return. I held my breath, afraid to exhale, believing if I remained still, time would also remain still.

Binh came back moments later and apologized. He did not explain his abrupt disappearing act. We moved on to dessert, and Binh poured some cognac. Mama made a beautiful caramel flan, but I did not trust myself to eat it. My body overheated, and my mind wandered down a dark path of violence. I imagined charging at Binh with a katana and piercing the sword between his eyes. I wanted to tear the fake eyelids off Nga and douse her hair with kerosene.

I stood up.

"Sit down," Binh said.

I kicked my chair back with one foot and pounded my knuckles on the table. I screamed at the top of my lungs. "Quỷ!" I called him a demon.

Mama jumped back. She clutched her necklace.

Nga's eyes opened wide and her lips quivered.

My stepdad calmly said, "Your daughter needs psychiatric help. She is out of control. She is dangerous. Do you see how she suddenly attacked me like that? Calling me a demon?"

"I am not crazy," I screamed. "You're the devil." I threw my chopsticks at him and when I missed, I picked up my plate and flicked it like a frisbee. "I hate you." I hurled my glass of Mountain Dew at his face. He dodged the tumbler, making me even angrier.

My stepdad smiled a wicked, evil smile. I knew then he had won. He wanted to get rid of me, and I gave him a solid reason to lock me up. The floodgates opened. Rivulets turned into a violent gush as tears streamed down my face, into my mouth, and along my jawline. My nose was stuffy, and the harder I sniffed to control the waterworks, the more I suffocated.

I was barely sixteen, and I'd had my first meltdown. Binh picked up the phone to call the police. Mama reached out to hug me, but rage burned within me, and I denounced her touch. The look of hurt and rejection on her face would haunt me for years. I was as angry with her as I was with Binh and Nga. I wanted nothing more than to die, to disappear, to vanish before their eyes.

I told myself I didn't need them. Who cared about good grades and living a pious life? Who could afford civility and humility? Wasn't life about "me" and what I could take, not give? I lost all hope. I did not feel human anymore. Like a caged tiger, I had paced back and forth far too long in my small cell. It was time to be free.

Mama hung up the phone before my stepdad could talk to the dispatcher. She slowly approached me and gingerly wrapped her arms around me. I let my pent-up anger and frustrations go. I howled and wailed. As my tears soaked her shirt, I dug my face harder into her shoulder.

"I'm sorry, Mama." I apologized over and over but my words did not make sense.

I don't recall when Nga left or when Binh went to the porch for a cigarette. I barely recall my mama tucking me into bed. I lay in my room shivering despite the heat and humidity outside. I called out to Ace in my mind and begged him to take me away. I prayed to God that he'd bring me home because I didn't want to live this life anymore. I begged Mr. and Mrs. Van to get me and take me back to Seattle. Even as I screamed in my mind, my voice box never opened, and I fell asleep, alone and hopeless.

Ace's birthday came and went. I feigned sickness and told him I'd make it up to him later. I harnessed all my energy to sound enthusiastic and wished him a happy birthday. I told him my mama wanted to invite him over for dinner to celebrate. My last words to him were, "I love you."

Friday afternoon, two days after Ace's birthday, I came home from helping Mrs. Poot Poot with her garden to find the house empty. Mrs. Poot Poot, an elderly woman who lived a few mobile homes down, got that nickname because she passed gas all the time. She was also hard of hearing and happily waved whenever anyone yelled out, "Good morning, Poot Poot."

I walked into the kitchen to get a glass of water and nearly tripped over a suitcase and two bags. I knelt and unzipped one of the bags. My LA Gears shoes, a couple of white-washed jeans, overalls…my clothes and belongings.

"Mama?" I called out, but she did not answer.

I pushed the door to her bedroom and saw her napping on the bed. I sat down and watched the rise and fall of her chest. I caressed her soft, smooth hand. She snored softly. I blipped her lips like she used to do when I was little but she didn't wake.

I snuggled up to her and lifted her arm around me like the old days when we slept together and I would curl up in her arms. More than anything I wanted to be six years old again and feel safe. I closed my eyes and thought of my cousin Tree. I missed him so much but he was living his life with his wife and children. I thought about Katrina and Mrs. Van showering me with Christmas gifts and Mr. Van reading me bedtime stories. I remembered how Uncle Skyler performed the Heimlich maneuver on Ms. Magdaleine to save her from choking. I wanted nothing more than to be back at Homestead Apartments with my friends and Auntie Diep. As ridiculous as she was, Auntie Diep was always cheerful and bright. She stood out like a turd in a swimming pool with her bright, mismatched clothes and loud, effervescent personality.

I closed my eyes and exhaled. I turned over and looked at my mama. She looked old to me. Being this close, I saw her facial lines and shockwaves of gray hair. The creases on her forehead and the character marks around her lips held secrets I'd never hear. I wondered if they were grooves of sorrow or joy. I counted the lines and wondered which ones were because of me. Did I bring her lines of pride or lines of shame?

My eyes misted, and I wiped them quickly to hide any trace of pity. I kissed Mama…not the American way with my lips, but the Vietnamese way, with my nose. I inhaled her essence and sniffed her cheeks, her skin, her bones. I nuzzled closer, and she stirred beside me. She stroked my hair and sang a song. I did not know the lyrics or the song, but the warm tone of her voice soothed me, and the melody wrapped me in peace.

"Thủy-Tiên," Mama said, "my daughter, listen to me carefully."

I nodded and pulled my mama's body closer to mine.

"I think we are destined to live apart."

I shook my head, unwilling to accept that.

"I once saw a fortune teller. She told me you were a wood tiger and that tiger girls have very strong personalities. They are more cunning than we give them credit for. My daughter, you are smarter and more strong-willed than me and you cannot thrive in the shadow of a weak boar."

My stepfather was born the year of the pig. I knew the boar referenced my stepdad.

"If we are to survive, we must live apart."

"What are you saying?" I searched her face for answers. "I saw the suitcase and bags. Are you sending me away?"

Mama's face turned pink and her eyes moistened. I wiped the wetness away.

"The Americans say if you love something, set it free. I am going to set you free."

"Where?" I asked. "I don't want to leave you."

"I have a plan," Mama said. "I am going to get my OMD so I can practice acupuncture and herbal medicine. When the timing is right, I am going to leave him."

I sat up and smiled. It was the best news ever.

"This will be two failed marriages for me. As a Catholic and a Vietnamese woman, you must understand how wrong and shameful this is. It means I can never marry again. No man will want me."

"Of course they will. Don't say that. You are beautiful and smart. You're funny and a good cook. You deserve someone who is not going to compete with you or feel inferior to you."

"I would not be worthy of another love if I cannot hold on to the ones I had."

"That's not true." I flung my arm around Mama's waist and rested my cheek on her bosom.

"Promise me you will graduate high school with honors and go to college. And I will promise to get my degree and become an acupuncturist. Then it will be the two of us again."

"What about Ace?" I asked. "Will I still get to see him?"

"That is up to you," Mama said.

"Where are you sending me?" I asked. "For how long?"

"My daughter," Mama said. "We leave soon. I cannot tell you but soon you will see." She kissed me on my head. "I know, sweet girl. I know."

"What do you know?" I asked.

"I know about your stepdad," Mama said. "I may not like conflict, but I am not stupid or blind."

"You mean you know about him and that lady, Nga? And the dirty magazines and videos?" I asked.

Mama nodded.

"Did you know he threatened to shoot me until I was paralyzed in a wheelchair?"

Mama did not answer. She pulled me into her embrace and squeezed tightly. I felt droplets of water slide down my forehead.

We drove in silence down to San Marcos, a suburb of San Diego, known for its pristine beachfront properties, close-knit communities, highly-rated schools, and blooming commerce.

I did not get to say goodbye to Ace. My stepdad tossed my belongings into the backseat, and then he and my mama whisked me away to southern California. My stepdad knew a woman who lived in San Marcos with her husband and two sons. He said she had always wanted a daughter and would love me the moment she saw me. Binh had known her back in Vietnam and attested she'd be the authoritarian I needed, both rigid in discipline and soft in compassion. She had the reputation back in Vietnam of turning corrupt men to reverent believers and unwieldy leeches to agreeable women. Her formula for love and punishment transformed even the vilest, rebellious souls into God-fearing, humble servants of all that was holy.

She sounded as scary as hell.

We pulled up to a large house in a gated community nestled in a quiet cul-de-sac. Healthy palm trees, birds of paradise, manicured hedges, and river rocks nestled in the lush garden along the cobblestone walkway.

The house was at least three thousand square feet, with two floors, a three-car garage, and a mailbox that came with keys. I was going to be living in style. My stepdad rang the doorbell and a petite woman with a high forehead and a tiny mouth opened the door. Everything about her was small, except for her forehead and hair. She looked odd with her tiny waist, high cheekbones, long manicured nails, and stiletto shoes. She was barely over five feet tall and without her shoes, I suspected she was four-foot nine inches tall. She wore a black jumpsuit and a white tennis visor. She smelled like lavender and lye. I guessed she was Binh's age or shy of sixty.

"Oh, it has been a long time." Her mousy voice squeaked like a violin that needed tweaking. She hugged my stepdad with a familiarity usually reserved for siblings. She embraced my mama with zeal and expressed how fortunate she was to finally meet her. One look at me and she nearly fainted with excitement. She clasped me tight and ushered me inside. She scurried along the hallway and fluttered into the kitchen, where she invited us to sit as she proceeded to make hot tea. I took note of my surroundings, impressed with the spotless kitchen, neatly arranged cookbooks in alphabetical order by title, and canned veggies in the cupboards, with the labels facing outward in order from artichoke to yams.

"This is Auntie Nhung," my stepdad said. "She will be taking care of you."

"And my husband Dan," she screeched. "He will be here soon with our sons Lộc and Hiếu. How was your drive here?" She peeled and sliced three cinnamon persimmons and arranged them neatly on a plate. One of the slices was thicker than the rest, so she took a thin sliver off to make them of equal width.

Mama chit-chatted about the weather and traffic. Binh helped himself to the persimmons and ate three slices before Mama finished one.

A man's voice called from the entryway and in came a tall, heavyset man with blue eyes and a red beard. He wore golfing shorts, a polo shirt, and a tweed flat cap. His lumbering walk made him look goofy, like a big buffoon. If ever there were an odd couple, these two took the trophy. Dan stood a good foot, three inches taller than his wife. Two Vietnamese men plodded behind him. One of them wore glasses, making his eyes look huge, like a tarsier. He had thin, receding hair. He wore Bermuda shorts and socks that rode up to his knees. He was a thick-built man with wide shoulders and rabbit teeth that protruded even when he closed his mouth. He looked thirty, but when he spoke, he sounded like a child. His eyes must have been bigger than his brain. I was introduced to Loc, Nhung's eldest son, who blushed and told me I was pretty.

The other man slothed behind Dan in his banana pants, Michael Jackson leather jacket, red bandana, and one white glove. He reminded me of Binh's youngest son, Phan. His face was narrow, hijacked with pimples, and his teeth took refuge behind metal braces. He had a small mouth like his mother and his narrow wombat eyes creeped me out. He had the same high forehead as Auntie Nhung and could have been her younger brother. His name was Hiếu, and he was going to be a junior in high school like me. Odd, because he looked twenty-five.

I had entered the twilight zone.

11. THE YELLOW JACKET (SUMMER-FALL 1990)

My farewell to Mama seared my heart. We both knew this would be difficult but necessary. We were on a mission to graduate from school and rendezvous back in Seattle. I wished Mama luck with acupuncture school and promised to stay on track with my education. She promised to give Ace my new address and Auntie Nhung's home phone number.

Mama gave me a dozen kisses, and with wetness in her eyes, she got in the car and disappeared down the road. I ran behind the car and watched it exit the gated community. I walked back to the house, where Auntie Nhung stood at the front entrance waiting for me. She opened her arms, and I melted into her tiny embrace. This stranger was all I had. I cried and let the fears, anger, and anxiety drain from my body. A sense of relief flowed through me as if a weight had been lifted.

Inside, Dan offered me a beverage, but I declined and thanked him. Loc and Hieu fawned over me like a shiny new toy. Loc, the eldest with bucked teeth, wanted to show me to my room. Hieu offered to help me unpack.

"Give her some space, boys," Dan said. "You're fighting over her like she's a puppy."

Auntie Nhung giggled and surprised me by speaking English fluently. "Lọc, you can show Christine to her room."

"Actually," I said, "you can call me Amy. I became a citizen and legally changed it to Amy."

"Oh, well, we registered you at the school under Christine," Dan said.

"You did?" I asked. "Wow, that was fast."

"It is too late and too much of a hassle to change it now," Auntie Nhung said. "School starts in less than three weeks."

"I'm sure it can be changed. I'll just talk to them—"

"I said it is too late." Auntie Nhung looked at me sternly and pulled her lips inward into a pucker.

Instinct told me to shut my mouth and drop the subject.

She smiled sweetly and put her arm around my waist. "It's just that we jumped through a lot of hoops to get you enrolled in school with short notice, and the administration office had been closed for the summer. Why don't you get settled in? The boys can show you around. The three of you will have to share the bathroom upstairs, so don't take too long in the morning. Use the timer in the bathroom. Each person gets fifteen minutes."

"We'll go over the ground rules and house chores over dinner," Dan said.

My stomach growled when Dan mentioned food. I pressed my tummy to quiet it down.

"Someone's hungry," Auntie Nhung said. "Since today is a special occasion with you joining our family, you can have seconds and dessert."

"Yay." Loc clapped his hand. "Dessert." His eyes opened wide, and his smile showed a lot of yellow teeth.

I smiled weakly. I supposed I should be grateful but thought it odd she would even say that. Food restrictions and portion control were never an issue after I came to the US. Mama, Tree, and I were blessed with government subsidies and homemade meals from our community of friends. We ate what we wanted, when we wanted, and as much as we wanted.

Hieu and Loc helped me with my bags, and I followed them up the stairs. The spacious and tidy home smelled of lemon and pine. My bedroom located above the garage with a window that overlooked the driveway was quaint and charming, although it befitted a little six-year-old princess more than a sixteen-year-old girl. The twin-size bed had two pillows covered in pink-and-white ruffled pillowcases, pink sheets, and a pink-and-white polka dot comforter. Stuffed animals rested in the center and claimed a third of the bed. A full-length mirror leaned against one of the walls, and a few framed posters of horses hung throughout the room. A family photo of Dan, Auntie Nhung, and their sons adorned the nightstand, and another family portrait rested on top of the dresser. Having pictures of them and none of my family and friends made me uneasy.

"Do you need help unpacking and putting things away?" Hieu asked. He unzipped my duffle bag, but I touched his hand to stop him. I did not want him going through my things. He quickly pulled his hand away as if my touch burned him and my closeness repelled him. He stepped back and paused before abruptly leaving the room. He ran down the stairs.

Loc followed him. "I better help set the table."

What oddlings. I dismissed their abrupt departure and took comfort in being alone for a few minutes to collect my thoughts and let reality set in. Memories of Seattle and my friends made me sad. Mama's and Ace's smiling faces filled my thoughts. I willed myself not to cry. Be strong. This was temporary, and I would see them again soon. I shoved my belongings in the drawers and hung up a couple of jackets. I stepped into the bathroom to freshen up and put my toiletries in the corner by the outlets. The smell of seasoned, grilled meat wafted up the stairs and beckoned me to come down.

Dan was in the kitchen wearing a frilly apron too small for his big frame. He wrapped his arm around Auntie Nhung and kissed her on the neck. He looked up and smiled at me. He had kind eyes and a simplicity to him that made me trust his genuine warmth. He carved the roast and placed each slice neatly on a platter of roasted vegetables.

Auntie Nhung orchestrated her sons' movements. "Get the green napkins. Take out the square bowl. No, make it the round, blue ones. Get the pitcher of water out of the fridge."

"Is there anything I can do to help?" I asked.

"You can help with the gravy," Dan said. "Over there. Just ladle it into the gravy boat, which is in that cupboard."

"Okay," Auntie Nhung said. "Come, come." She waved me over and patted the seat next to her. "Your place is next to me."

I sat down to her right at the round table and admired the setting and food. A bowl of minestrone, a beet and goat cheese salad, buttered rolls, and cranberry-orange relish filled the table. Dan placed the platter of beef and vegetables in the center and took his place on Auntie Nhung's left.

"Thank you, dear," Auntie Nhung said, "this looks delicious." Loc and Hieu chimed in with their thanks. I followed suit. "Now, each night, we like to go around the table and share one thing great and one thing bad about our day. We discuss it as a family over dinner. Christine, why don't you—"

"Could you call me Amy, please?" I asked. "Or my Vietnamese name, Thủy-Tiên?"

"Very well," she said. "Now, why don't you start and tell us—"

"I'm sorry, do you have any Mountain Dew or 7-Up?" I asked. "Any soda or juice?"

"We do not drink soda and juice in this house unless it's a holiday or someone's birthday. Too much sugar. Our body is a temple and we must take care of it." Auntie Nhung pursed her lips again and cut into her meat like she was tearing into a fresh kill.

"Do you say grace?" I asked.

"Say what?" Loc asked.

"A prayer?" I said. "Do you give thanks before you eat?"

"No," Auntie Nhung said. "We're Buddhists."

I looked at Dan. Was he Buddhist as well? He did not look up from his plate of food, and Auntie Nhung did not speak again, so I, too, kept my mouth shut. I made the sign of the cross like I had seen Mama do and said a silent prayer.

Dan cleared his throat. "Why don't I start?"

"Thank you, dear," Auntie Nhung said sweetly. "And boys, let's not interrupt Dad." She glanced at me briefly, but I caught the undertone of her message. I interrupted one too many times, and she was not amused. Another interruption would be a grave mistake.

Dan raised his glass of water. "I would like to make a toast to Amy. Her joining our family has been a great thing in my day. We hope you'll come to see us like family and enjoy your stay with us this year."

We all raised our glasses of water and clinked before sipping. The consensus around the table was that I was a welcomed surprise. I certainly felt like a novelty but wondered if that would quickly wear off. Dan talked about not getting a promotion at work. He was a graphic designer and ready to take on new projects as well as manage a team. Instead, he got an individual contributor raise and bonus but still reported to Gerald, a man he felt was not fit to manage people. Auntie Nhung praised him for putting his name in the hat for the promotion and agreed his company was blind for not seeing the talent Dan offered.

"Their loss, dear." Auntie Nhung offered her lips to Dan, and they kissed again.

Loc talked about gaining a pretty sister this year and was impressed that I played badminton. "I like sports and working out and staying fit." He flexed his muscles. I chuckled. He seemed so innocent. "No offense, Dad, but you work too much and are getting pudgy. You need to work out."

Dan pretended to be hurt and sucked in his stomach and cheeks. He was our comic relief, and I found him endearing. I could see how Auntie Nhung fell in love with him.

"I am down for playing badminton or volleyball or tennis any time," I said to Loc. "And you can show me some workouts. We can lift weights together."

"Oh, honey," Auntie Nhung said, "girls should not lift weights. You can do yoga or aerobics." I disagreed but did not push back. I winked at Loc when no one was looking. It was our little secret. He blushed and winked back.

"So what was the one bad thing that happened today?" I asked Loc.

"Nothing," he answered, "but I guess beets and goat cheese salads aren't my favorite. At least I can have seconds on everything else, plus dessert. I'm a growing boy." He flexed his muscles again.

I smiled. I loved that he found joy in the smallest things. Hieu shared his highlight of finishing his chores in record time, but his low point was scrubbing the toilets without gloves.

"What happened to your gloves?" Auntie Nhung asked. "Did you leave them in the backyard again? You know they are not garden gloves."

"But I like the way they fit," Hieu said. "and they are thick so the dirt doesn't soak through. The rubber ones are way better than the cloth ones."

Auntie Nhung let the topic of garden gloves versus cleaning gloves go. She asked me to share with the family my positive and negative points of the day. I struggled to pick one thing decent because I didn't see anything good about my day.

My hesitation irritated Auntie Nhung. She wiped her tiny lips with her napkin and threw it on her lap. "If you can't think of one good thing, let me remind you—"

"It's not that, Auntie Nhung." I interrupted her again. I had to think of something fast. "There have been a few good things today." I stalled to buy time and racked my brain. "Well, I am thankful to you all for your kindness in receiving me into your home and making me feel like a part of your family. And, um, I appreciate the care in getting my room ready for me, not to mention getting me enrolled in school."

Auntie Nhung nodded her approval. "We are excited you are here. It will be more balanced now having a girl at the house. These guys gang up on me."

Dan chuckled. "Don't believe her. She's the boss. She bullies us." Dan leaned over and gave his wife a peck on the lips. It was clear by the way Dan catered to her whims that he was whipped. He doted on her, kissed her often, and complimented her constantly. They must have magnets implanted in their lips because the two of them kissed all the time.

I yearned for Ace. "Can I have the house phone number and address?"

"What for?" Auntie Nhung asked.

"Um, in case there is an emergency?"

"Why don't we go over the rules and expectations?" Auntie Nhung handed her empty plate to Loc.

He stood and placed her plate in the dishwasher. He came back with apple pie.

"Now, on the refrigerator, there is a cleaning schedule. Each week the three of you will rotate so you're not doing the same thing. My boys will show you how to clean the bathrooms, the floors, and all the surfaces. We use specific products and materials for different things. Tomorrow is floor day. Chris…I mean, Amy…you will vacuum. One of the boys will sweep the outside, front and back, and the other will mop the floors inside the house."

"Once school starts," Dan said, "you need to do your homework right when you get home. You can have a snack first, but no food is allowed in the bedroom."

"We eat dinner together, and afterward, if you still have homework or need to prepare for an exam, then you can go back upstairs." Auntie Nhung cut the apple pie into eight equal pieces and handed Dan the first slice. "Television is a treat, and we watch together as a family. We don't want your brain to melt from the garbage on TV. You can read a book or do something creative."

"I lift weights," Loc said.

"What do you do, Hieu?" I asked.

"I like Legos," Hieu said. "I'm pretty good at building things. I'll show you my collection."

"In the mornings," Dan said, "there is a fifteen-minute limit in the bathroom on school days. Be sure to use the timer."

"Same goes with phone calls," Auntie Nhung said. "Fifteen minutes maximum. Anything else, dear?"

"One other thing," Dan said. "We have a penalty jar. No foul language allowed, and no backtalking. Each week you will get a ten-dollar allowance. Breaking a rule results in a hefty five-dollar fine. At the end of the month, one of you will get what is in the penalty jar, based on whomever we feel was exceptionally good or achieved something spectacular. The jar remains untouched if there is nothing worth rewarding that month."

My head reeled. I swallowed my tongue and refrained from scoffing at their rigid rules.

"I always win the jar," Hieu said. "He's always breaking rules."

That surprised me. I took Loc as the sweeter and more innocent one. I couldn't imagine him cussing, backtalking, or heaven forbid, using the wrong cleaning agent for the kitchen that was meant for the bathroom.

Auntie Nhung patted my knee. "We will not have any penalties for you the first week as you're learning, but after you are told once, we expect you to get it right the next time."

That night I dreamed about scrubbing toilets and getting locked in a room full of mice. My fairy godmother was Dan, and he brought me magic red ruby slippers. If I clicked my heels twice, the toilet sparkled, and my princess bed flew me home. It flew over Ace's Supra and kept going. I screamed for him, but I had no voice. I reached for him, but he did not see me. He was lost to me, and I could not get off the flying bed.

Then down the rabbit hole I tumbled and crashed with a thud on an underground nest of yellow jackets. The colony arose and swarmed around my head. I flailed my arms and struck the queen. Her yellow and black body charged at me and stung me repeatedly with her poison. I fell to the ground in pain, writhing in agony, withering to dust. Auntie Nhung hovered over me with her beady eyes and wasp-like wings and watched me die.

12. LOVECRAFTIAN (FALL 1990-WINTER 1991)

My first semester as a junior at San Marcos High School could be described in one word: Lovecraftian. Under the veneer of normal teenage life, where the jocks hung out with cheerleaders and the nerds hung out alone in a quiet, invisible corner of the school, bubbled a situation that changed my perception of mankind and taught me to trust my instincts. People were the same on the inside as they were on the outside if you looked closely enough and paid attention. Humans are flawed creatures, and vanity had a way of showing its true colors. I learned about vanity in San Marcos but lived with it at home.

In April 1986, the phenomenon of Halley's Comet had captured the attention of my sixth-grade class. Every store sold rubber balls with shiny streamers attached to them and every kid played with them at recess. When the Circle K convenience store down the street from Homestead Apartments began selling them, I saved my quarters and bought one. My friends and I tossed them high in the air and watched the shimmering tail as the ball came down and bounced off the ground.

In my art class, a girl named Carina resembled one of those rubber Halley's Comet balls, with her silky, long, blue, pink, and purple hair attached to a head as clueless as a rubber ball. Like me, she was Vietnamese. Her parents were refugees of the Vietnam War. She was rebellious like most teenagers and wild like some of the kids of my generation who didn't fit in with any culture. She appeared to be a loner like me, and we instantly connected and became friends. She introduced me to her circle of friends, Phuong, Lily, and Mary. The five of us banded together, ate lunch together, and enjoyed gossiping about others. I let them cheat off me in class whenever we had a test, and sometimes I did their assignments for them.

I desperately wanted to belong to a tribe, so I let my moral compass go south. I needed my new friends to survive the loneliness of being separated from those whom I loved. They needed me to pass their exams and get good grades to keep their parents off their backs. We had the perfect symbiotic relationship, although not a healthy one. Over time I became one of the mean girls who made fun of everyone and looked down on others. No teacher was safe from my snide remarks, and no student escaped my condescending, judgmental snickers. My tribe built an impenetrable force field around us, and we shielded each other from the ugly truth—that we were the true rejects and outcasts, not everyone else.

The sisterhood I had with Carina, Phuong, Lily, and Mary was tangible, strong, and believable while it lasted. The girls smoked cigarettes, skipped classes, and stole from their parents, and while I never succumbed to these habits, my heart marched in rhythm with theirs. Sometimes I gave in to their cajoling and peer pressure. I took a puff or two of a cigarette or skipped a class to prove I wasn't a prude.

We all hated our home life and thought we were better than our siblings. I did not have siblings, of course, but I knew I was smarter than Loc and Hieu. The adults in our lives were old-school, traditional as hell, overbearing, strict, embarrassing to be around, and did not understand that we wanted one simple thing—to be left alone. We sought refuge in music and fed off each other's sarcasm.

At home, life with Auntie Nhung was unbearable, but somehow I managed to stay on the other side of the line drawn in the sand. I stuck to the rules and held my tongue, lest I get punished and lose my allowance to the penalty jar.

Each time I paged Ace, he called me back, but Auntie Nhung yanked the phone away so that I never spoke to him. Why hadn't he visited? I worried he had stopped loving me and had forgotten about me. Had he moved on already? I resented him every time I thought he had given up. I still loved him with all my being and held on to what little hope I had left. Mama assured me she had given Ace the address where I lived. Auntie Nhung was so strict with phone usage that even with my mama, I was restricted to fifteen-minute conversations.

Auntie Nhung gave me just enough air to breathe but never enough to take full breaths. She gave me just enough rope to move about but never long enough to feel free. She fed me enough food I didn't starve, yet I never felt satisfied. Gluttony was a sin and gaining weight the ultimate disgrace to the body that served as our temple. I lived in a box that was not wide enough or tall enough. With my new family, I felt like the maid, the stepchild, the black swan, and the ugly duckling all rolled into one. Sometimes I felt like the prized possession perched on a pedestal in a curiosity shop, and other times I felt like a social experiment to see how thin my patience would grow before I snapped. Even I wondered how long Auntie Nhung could press me under her thumb before I collapsed.

She told me she had always wanted a daughter but under the same breath dropped matchmaking hints that I would make a great wife for one of her sons. I shuddered at the thought of being married to Brains or Brawns, nicknames I gave to Hieu and Loc. While the boys were nice to me, they were odd and mentally slow. Hieu looked at me with puppy love eyes and lust on his face. On several occasions, he rubbed up against me in the kitchen with a hard-on and acted like nothing was out of the ordinary. I dared not think about the fantasies he had of me when he was alone in his room or the shower. Loc only cared about bodybuilding and fitness. He spent every spare moment in the garage lifting weights. Girls did not exist to him.

I had my second meltdown while I was still sixteen. One day halfway through the school year, I skipped lunch and made a beeline for the only payphone on school grounds. I would page Ace and confront him. This time, there would be no auntie to rip the phone from me and no fifteen-minute time limit. I would skip my next class if necessary.

A girl on the payphone rambled about her favorite flavor of ice cream. I wanted her to hurry up with the call. I shifted my weight from one foot to the other. My palms sweated. I crossed my arms and tapped my foot. She looked at me and rolled her eyes. She resumed talking, so I tapped her shoulder. I was not going to be ignored.

She covered the receiver. "What?"

"Can you hurry up, please?" I asked. "I have an emergency."

She looked me up and down and rolled her eyes. She twirled the telephone cord and turned her back to me. I tapped her again, but she pretended I was not there. I waited only a split second before I ripped the phone from her hand and slammed it on the receiver.

"What the hell?" she yelled. "You've got some nerve, chink."

"I asked you politely," I said.

"Wait your turn."

She picked up the phone again and when I reached for it, she held it behind her. We scrambled and struggled for it until she clobbered me on the face with the phone. A sharp pain shot up my nose. Drops of red dripped from my face to the ground. All the pent-up anger, sadness, frustration, and self-control erupted. The she-hulk in me exploded out of my skin. I felt powerful and strong, invincible, and lawless.

I grabbed her hair and wrapped it around my fist. I slammed her face over and over and over into the side of the payphone. "I. Just. Want. My. Damn. Phone. Call."

She sat on the ground holding her face and whimpering.

Devoid of empathy, I made my call and waited for Ace to call me back. I kicked the girl now crumpled on the cement. "What's the matter?"

Her black eyeliner smeared around her eyes, and her face swelled.

The phone finally rang, and I quickly picked it up. "Honey?"

"Christine?" Ace sounded happy and relieved. "Baby, is that you? God, what happened? I've been trying to call you and find you but—"

"But what?" I asked. No answer. "Hello?" The phone went dead.

I was ready to punch the girl but froze. The cold eyes looking back at me belonged to Mrs. Jenkins, the school principal. I scanned my surroundings. An audience of faculty members and students stared back at me. The school nurse tended to my victim. Our blood mixed and covered everything—our clothes, our shoes, the phonebooth, the ground. I swallowed the dry lump of coal in my throat.

The principal had her finger on the receiver and hung up my call. "My office. Now."

Mrs. Jenkins grabbed my wrist and tugged at me to follow but I did not yield. I was done yielding. I was tired of authority.

I lost my senses and attacked her. "She started it." I pointed at the brunette whose nose was smashed and crooked. A massive hematoma developed on her forehead. She looked like a cosmic being, an alien from outer space. I laughed with delirium. "She hit me first."

Mrs. Jenkins did not care. To her, I was probably another Asian kid who didn't belong at her school much less her country. She was much taller and heavier than I was, but I was fast, feisty, and enraged. My arms and legs pounded away while my demons took control. Two people pulled me off and dragged me away like a wild monkey. My body drooped and became dead weight.

After that incident, Carina, Lily, Phuong, and Mary kept their distance. I was a powder keg, and once again, a ticking time bomb. The school suspended me indefinitely. Auntie Nhung flipped her lid, and I endured two long hours of her tongue lashing. No one rescued me. Loc and Hieu hid in their rooms. Dan wouldn't be home until eight o'clock.

"Do you know what I used to do to girls like you back in Vietnam?" Auntie Nhung asked. I said nothing, so she told me. "I threw them to the tigers of the jungle and let my thirsty comrades on the Ho Chi Minh Trail teach ungrateful shits like you a lesson."

I cringed. I lowered my eyes and stared at the carpet fibers beneath my feet. Her tiny frame loomed over me while I knelt on the floor with my head down and hands in my lap.

"That's right. I'd stand watch while my brothers raped those women. Their cries were their only salvation."

I lifted my head and stared at her. "You did what?"

"Shut up," she screamed. "You are really testing me, aren't you? We took you in and gave you a home. You've been ungrateful and need to be punished. Only then will you feel cleansed and free of guilt." She was a raving lunatic.

"You're mad," I said. "I have done everything you've asked of me. Every day I scrub your toilets, mop your floors, clean your windows. Not once did I complain. Not once did I break a rule."

"Is that so?" she said. "Don't think I didn't notice you watched television when you got home from school."

"Loc and Hieu told on me?"

"They didn't have to. I always leave the channel on seven and I'd find it on another channel when I got home. My boys know better, and they are good kids."

"You've got serious problems," I said. "And God will punish you for what you did to those women."

She slapped me. "That's where you are wrong. I have been rewarded. Look around you. What do you see? My big house. My doting husband. My two sons."

"Whom you've manipulated to serve you," I said. "Can't you see you're the one being punished, not rewarded, or has your vanity given you glaucoma? Your sons have the mental and emotional intelligence of rocks and your husband doesn't love you. He fears you."

She slapped me again. "You're jealous of me. You will never have this because you are too ruined to ever achieve greatness."

The sting of her hand invigorated me. I liked the pain and wanted more of it. I lunged at her and clawed at her throat. My fingernails dug into her face, and my teeth clamped down on her shoulder. We rivaled for dominance, rolling around on the floor and chasing after each other until I slipped on the freshly waxed floors.

Auntie Nhung snarled and cackled. Her laugh started as a low rumble from her belly and escalated into a high-pitched hyena's laugh from her throat. "Your mother is ashamed of you. Your father abandoned you. Even your boyfriend doesn't want you."

"Lies!" I threw the salt and pepper shakers at her. I knew what she was doing. Auntie Nhung chipped away at my armor and stripped my defenses.

Perhaps she was right. I was reckless, spoiled, disrespectful, and brought dishonor to my mama. My dad never fought for me. He didn't want me. He never called or wrote to me. I had always been a burden to my mama. I brought destruction and sadness. All those times of joy and peace in my life were because my mama and my cousin put me first in their life. I never did anything for them. I had been selfish to only think of myself. Gimme gimme gimme. Take take take.

I broke down in tears and sobbed. I did not want to fight. I wanted to disappear and not live that life anymore.

I returned to school after two weeks and would be expelled if I so much as looked at a teacher wrong. Auntie Nhung watched me like a salivating bear. One false move and she'd happily eat me alive. When I wasn't on my hands and knees scrubbing an imaginary smudge off the floors or polishing the silverware for the tenth time, I pulled clumps of soggy hair out of the drains and counted each grain of rice in a fifty-pound bag. She tormented me by making up ludicrous chores.

Dan felt sorry for me. He snuck me fashion magazines and art supplies to keep me sane. An article called for all artists and poets ages fourteen to eighteen to submit their projects in a statewide competition sponsored by the San Diego Chargers football team as part of their Hire-A-Youth program. I decided to enter both because I had nothing else to do.

I titled my poem "Redemption." It was about coming back from shame. I wrote several versions of it, but the one I sealed and gave to Dan never made it to the post office. It slipped out of his briefcase, and Auntie Nhung burned it. It was the first fight the couple had in the time I lived with them. Dan stood up to her and fought for me, but in the end, he lost the argument and slept on the couch for two nights.

Night after night after everyone went to bed, I did some stippling under the moon's watch as she shined her light through my window. Using the quill pen and ink that Dan slipped into my dresser, I dabbed hundreds of thousands of dots on an eleven-by-fourteen artist's pad of paper until the dots resembled actress Michelle Yeoh's beautiful face. The drawing took me a week to finish. Pride filled my chest over how detailed and intricate the jewels of her dress turned out, the density of the pigmentation in her hair, and the light shading of her skin. Dan sealed it carefully and did not address the packaging until he got to the post office.

I took the opportunity to write letters to Amy Chen in Hong Kong, to my seventh grade best friend Marina Ogawa in Renton, and Mr. and Mrs. Vanzwol in Kent. I never sent my letters to Amy and the Vanzwols because I didn't have their addresses. The only one I knew by heart was Marina's, and I told her not to write back. Writing the letters was therapeutic even though they'd never be answered.

It did not matter anyway. The only answer I wanted to receive was from God. Before I closed my eyes at night, I begged him to help me leave. I needed to find myself again. I needed to be happy. I wasn't thriving, and I so desperately wanted a second chance.

He told me to save my allowance and buy a one-way ticket to Seattle.

13. HELLO, MAMA (SPRING 1991)

Spring break arrived. I missed Mama and I begged her to drive down. I complained about the lonely winter break. The sunny, warm Christmas didn't have the magic of Seattle. I missed putting on my warm knit sweaters, gloves, and beanie and stepping out into the frost. I missed the snow and waking up to the glistening, white landscape of a true winter wonderland. I yearned to hear Mr. Van's deep voice as he jingled his bell and pretended he was Santa Claus. My heart ached for my childhood, and I wished I could relive those days again.

Hearing Mama's sweet voice was the balm my troubled soul needed. We spoke for seventeen minutes. I pushed my boundaries because I simply did not care anymore. I had survived the worst of Auntie Nhung and knew I could endure more. She was not my puppet master. I made that very clear.

Over spring break I kept my head down using the SAT and ACT exams as an excuse to stay home and study. Although I told myself it didn't matter whether I scored well on the exams or if I got into college, it went against my nature to be unprepared. While the family went to the zoo or SeaWorld, I humbly declined. Auntie Nhung was suspicious and did not like the idea of leaving me home unsupervised, but I gave her my most respectful and subservient promise. I encouraged Dan to spend time with his family and pointed out it would be one less ticket to buy and one less mouth to feed. He was reluctant, but financial planning was his love language.

I did not tell them about Mama's visit. Having her to myself was an exciting prospect I wanted to relish. The visit would be too awkward with Dan and Auntie Nhung hovering over us. I told Mama to come by herself. She didn't.

The doorbell rang. Excited and nervous, I ran to the door and swung it wide open. Mama stood there in a lovely yellow skirt and blouse. She had on a bonnet to keep the sun from scorching her light skin and giving her age spots. She had put on a lot of weight, and I was shocked. We embraced, and moisture leaked from our eyes.

"Hello, Mama."

"I know you told me to come alone, but…" Mama took my hand and led me outside.

My heart raced. I was unsure of what I would say to my stepdad or how I would react. His presence would put a damper on our visit, but at least Mama came. I reminded myself to be grateful for that. After all, all roses have thorns and sometimes you cannot have the beauty without the pain or the positives without the negatives.

I followed Mama to the driveway, and when I turned the corner, my knees buckled.

The Supra sat in the driveway.

Ace opened the door and held a bouquet in his hand. He scooped me up and held me tight. I breathed in his scent and squeezed him as hard as I could. The tears fell, and we stood there motionless for a long time. Neither one of us spoke. It was so unreal.

I finally broke away from our embrace. "I've dreamed so many times about this moment when I would see you again. I've missed you so much. You have no idea."

"I can't believe I'm here right now," Ace said. "We have your mom to thank for arranging this."

I turned to my mama and hugged her hard. I startled her by lifting her a couple of inches off the ground.

"Thank you, Mama!" A dozen kisses rained on her cheeks and hands. "I love you so much. Thank you!"

Joy and peace rose inside me at reuniting with the two people I loved most. I waved them into the house, and we sat down in the living room. I held both their hands and didn't let go for fear they'd disappear. My body floated, and my spirit soared.

"What time do you expect the family back?" Ace asked.

I wanted to kiss him so badly but didn't want Mama to feel awkward and disrespected. I held his hand and snuggled next to him on the loveseat. "I don't expect them home for another four or five hours."

"You look beautiful. You've lost some baby fat." He teased and kept his eyes on mine.

"Yes, I don't eat as much as I used to," I said. "Mama, you look lovely. Tell me everything."

Mama blushed and patted her thick arms. "I've gained too much weight as you can see."

"Too much good cooking in your kitchen?" I asked. "Any new recipes?"

"There is little time to cook now that I am enrolled in a naturopathic school," Mama said. "We dine out often. Sometimes your stepdad brings home food from the Asian Garden Mall. The studies keep me busy."

She rambled on about the qi flow of energy through the body and how each meridian was associated with an organ. She talked about how acupuncture and acupressure worked together and how fascinating the tiny needles pinpointed certain illnesses, stimulated relaxation, decreased pain, regulated blood flow, and brought peace to the brain.

"I practice on cadavers." She talked with great animation and passion.

It made me happy she had found something for herself. I wanted to know how things were between Binh and her but refrained from asking.

I summarized my school year for them, but I did not give them all the details because I did not want them to worry or stress out.

"I entered an art contest with the San Diego Chargers, and I've been studying for my ACT and SAT exams." I rested my hand on Ace's thigh. "I'm sorry our phone call ended so suddenly last time."

I told them about the altercation with the girl at the payphone but glossed over the broken nose and hematoma part. I wasn't sure how much Auntie Nhung had shared with my mama and stepdad, so I deviated down a less bumpy road.

I punched Ace's shoulder and gave him a charley horse. He jumped back in surprise. "What was that for?"

"Why didn't you rescue me from this hellhole?" I rubbed his shoulder like he was a wounded bird. "And what's the plan now?"

Mama and Ace didn't answer, so I bullied Ace to speak up. I pinched him.

"Ouch," Ace said. "You've gotten meaner, I see." He grinned, and I knew he was being playful. "I called your house a few times, but no one answered. Then I came to the house the following weekend, and your stepdad told me you were gone. I freaked out. He said you lived in San Diego and wouldn't give me your address or phone number. I prayed you'd page me so I could talk to you, and every time I returned the page, we got disconnected. Now, here we are eight months later."

"I counted on Mama to give you the address." I was confused. "They have me under surveillance here. I couldn't call collect to your beeper, and I didn't have Van's number memorized. But, Mama, you and I have spoken a few times, and you said nothing." I looked at Ace. "I thought you didn't love me anymore and had moved on."

"Honey, I never gave up." He kissed me tenderly on the forehead. "Your stepdad changed the phone number. I called one day, and there was a girl's voice on the answering machine. I was so excited thinking you came home, but I realized it wasn't your voice. And then your parents moved. I came to the mobile home, and it was for sale."

"What?" I said. "Mama, you moved? When? Where?"

"Business was not good," Mama said, "so we closed shop. I wanted to go to school so we moved back to Westminster northeast of the mall."

"And I went to the Phước Lộc Thọ mall to confront them, but the shop was a fabric store."

All these missed communications and passing ships. I shook my head. "So what is Bình doing now? Please tell me he's not doing real estate with Ms. Nga?"

Mama lowered her eyes, and I knew.

"Oh, Mama! This must be so hard for you." My anger flared, and I scowled. I stood and put my hands on my waist. "Oh, he's going to pay for this."

"Let it go, Thuỷ-Tiên," Mama said. "He is not worth it."

Unbelievable. How could she be so passive and laissez-faire about it all?

"Let him have his fun. Let him grow his real estate business and pay for my education. When the timing is right, I will divorce him and sue him for half his assets. Right now we have a marriage of convenience and perception. We sleep in separate beds and entertain together when we have to make an appearance. When the business went downhill—"

"That's because he's a poor businessman!" I said. "He gives everything away for free or at deep discounts so he can be popular." It infuriated me that my mama endured all of this. She had been caged all this time in a deceptive marriage.

"I have made friends at acupuncture school." Mama perked up. "They are all Vietnamese, and they are all men except me and Liễu. Your stepdad is jealous, but there is nothing he can do about it. I torture him by telling him I have to stay late with my new friends to study."

"Just be careful," I said. "I don't trust him, and he can get violent."

"He will not hurt me," Mama said. "He's got holes in his mouth that retain nothing, only empty promises and casual threats. Trust me, he never follows where his mouth leads."

"School will be out in two months," I said. "I hate the idea of you living with him and putting on a show. What about our plan of leaving California and heading back to Seattle? We can do that once my junior year ends. We have some time to make plans. We can stay with Mr. and Mrs. Van, or what about Uncle Skyler or—"

"Your mom and I talked about this in the car," Ace said. "We ran into each other at the grocery store, and that's how we reconnected. We think you should go up there first—"

I looked at them. I couldn't believe what they suggested. "No, absolutely not." I shook my head wildly and crossed my arms. I pouted like a child throwing a tantrum. "We go together. Forget about suing Binh. There are acupuncture schools in Washington. We have family and friends up there."

"But I found a new community in Westminster, and I don't want to transfer," Mama said. "How would I even pay for school?"

"Get a loan," I said. "Jean-Adrien and Katrina are loaded. I'm sure they can lend you money."

"Absolutely not," Mama said. "I am too old to be starting over with everything and living off other people's generosity. I hate that I cannot support myself and am stuck with your stepdad. But we all have to make sacrifices. You have to go first."

"That's right, honey," Ace said. "Finish high school, get your Washington state residency, and then go to college as an in-state student. The tuition is less."

"You're going with me, right?" I asked him.

He shook his head.

"What do you mean?" I screamed at them both. "You both made these decisions about my life without me? You're treating me like a kid. I'll be seventeen this summer." Ace pulled me into his arms, but I pushed him away. "And where are you going?"

"I reenlisted with the Navy," he said.

"You what?" I punched his chest and paced back and forth. I pulled at my hair. "Where will you be stationed? For how long? Why?"

Things unraveled fast. I had not expected this reunion to go this way.

"I'll be in Corpus Christi in Texas," Ace said. "I'll be close to my brother."

I put my face in my hands and cried. "I'll move to Texas then. I'll live with your brother."

"You can't." Ace wrapped his arms around me, and I did not fight him. "I get out in two years."

"Two years?" I bawled. "No." I shoved him. "This is a shitty plan. Come up with something else."

"I'm sorry honey," Ace said, "but my hands were tied. "IBM laid me off and told me to get a degree. I lost hope of finding you, so I reenlisted. The Navy will pay for my education."

Why did he have to do things the proper way? I wanted him to get off his high horse and run away with me. We would figure things out as we went. He wanted to set us up for a bright future, a solid one where we didn't have to struggle and put stress on our relationship. I called him a coward and a few other names. I could not accept this change in plans.

I hit him in the chest. "We can get through anything if we loved each other. Don't you love me enough?"

"I love you more than you know," he said. "I know this is not easy, but we have our whole life ahead of us. You're almost seventeen, and I'll be twenty-two in August. We're still young."

Gloom pervaded the last couple of hours of our afternoon together. It would be a while before I'd see them both again. Mama promised to escort me to Seattle after school let out. I would stay with a family friend in Aberdeen, Washington. Mr. and Mrs. Van planned to move to Arizona and retire. Skyler, Magdaleine, Katrina, and Jean-Adrien traveled too often and could not host me. My cousin Tree would remain in San Jose and raise his three kids. Not even Auntie Diep and Donald could take me in. They had their cozy family of three boys and no room for another person to live with them.

Like a hot potato, I was being passed around from household to household. I stood ramrod and narrowed my eyes. I needed to survive one year in Aberdeen, then I'd be free. I'd be at a university, living an independent life, and would have no one to answer to but me.

I relented, and together we worked out the details. I gave Ace my friend Marina's address in Washington and told him I would always keep in touch with her. If he and I ever lost touch, he could write to her, and she would know how to find me.

Saying goodbye to Mama and Ace was difficult. I did not want to let go of either of them. I loved them deeply. Why did there have to be so many farewells in my life? We made promises to be strong, to stay safe, and to never give up. Two years was an eternity.

Mama pried me off Ace so he could get in the car. They had to leave before Auntie Nhung got home. With afternoon traffic, it would take them two hours to get back to Westminster.

I watched them drive away and went back inside to an empty, lonely, sparkling clean house that felt like a prison. This house was no Hanoi Hilton, and I was not a prisoner of war, thankfully, but it was still hell on Earth, and I had to break out. I had to be free. I could not live under the roof of a Viet

Cong woman who stood guard while women were raped, who threw prisoners to the jungles of Vietnam to be slaughtered, and who freaking pursed her lips every single day because I was less significant to her than a dung beetle.

14. CONFESSION NIGHT (SPRING 1991)

My relationship with the Yellow Jacket remained tense. I lost all respect for Auntie Nhung knowing she was an accomplice to those violent crimes against women. It took all my willpower to be civil and respectful toward her. I knew not to bite the hand that fed me. I had a couple of months left of school, and the only way to endure it was to kill Auntie Nhung with kindness. I loathed her, but I would not turn into a monster like her. Hate would not consume me.

She did not forget my episodes of insubordination, but over time she swept them under the rug. The more polite and kind I was to Auntie Nhung, the more she accepted my theatrics. We both pretended nothing had happened, and because we were such convincing actors, I almost believed her kindness was genuine. I think she also almost believed I had converted from a child of damnation to one of salvation.

Loc and Hieu thought I had atoned for my transgressions and was back in their mother's good graces. The truth was I counted down the days to freedom. I focused my energy on ensuring I had no setbacks. Everything had to be smooth sailing or else I would never escape the cycle of mind control. Each day I did my chores and went the extra mile to help Loc and Hieu with their duties. The three of us made a pact that we would split the money in the penalty jar three ways no matter who won it.

Mama and Ace's visit gave me hope that I could set my course if I didn't allow little inconveniences to become major showstoppers. I saved all my allowance so that I could buy my plane ticket. I would prove to my naysayers, namely Binh and Auntie Nhung, that I was not a spoiled child who had lost her way. I could still be someone great and live the charmed life I deserved.

One spring evening we sat down as a family for dinner like we routinely did. It was confession night. The Yellow Jacket was in one of her rare benevolent moods and promised all topics were safe to discuss—there would be no judgment or punishment. She wanted to clear the air and start the month of May fresh, which meant leaving the worries and troubles behind with April. Having never participated in a confession night, I asked to go last. No one volunteered to go first, so Auntie Nhung voluntold her eldest son to go.

Loc cleared his throat and shifted in his seat. He stuttered as he confessed to watching television after school because he didn't want to miss an interview with Arnold Schwarzenegger. He changed the channel back to seven after he finished watching so that he wouldn't get caught. I held my breath for Auntie Nhung's reaction. Her boys were not so perfect after all.

"What did you learn from watching the interview?" Auntie Nhung took a small bite of her tenderloin and chewed slowly. I could tell she held back. She chewed the small piece of beef for what seemed like fifty times before she swallowed.

Meanwhile, Loc sweated. "Arnold is a seven-time Mr. Olympia champion. He holds the record of most wins, but Lee Haney may win his eighth one this year."

Auntie Nhung corrected Loc. "So he's tied. He doesn't hold the record if they both have seven titles."

He stuttered and fumbled his fork and knife. "I guess. Oh, and Arnold has a new movie coming out on July 3. It's Terminator Two. Can we go see it?"

"Did you learn anything else?" Auntie Nhung asked. "If you are going to break a rule, at least learn a life lesson or something valuable."

"Uh, well," Loc stammered. "Protein is the best for building muscle, like steak, chicken, fish, and eggs, and sugars make us fat, so I guess I'll skip dessert."

Loc came out of confession night alive. Who would get skinned next?

Dan volunteered. "So remember when Amy was going to enter that art and poetry contest?"

"Yes," Auntie Nhung said, "and I burned her poem because we do not reward bad behavior in this house by letting kids satisfy their itches."

"Well…" Dan said.

"What did you do, dear?" Auntie Nhung chewed her asparagus slowly and put her knife down.

"I sent in her drawing for the art competition," Dan said. "It was too good not to send in, and honestly, I did it for selfish reasons." Both the Yellow Jacket and I raised our eyebrows. What did he mean by selfish reasons? "First-prize winners in each category get cool stuff, including autographed Chargers memorabilia. Maybe she'll win, and I can convince her to give me the football swag."

"Wow, Dan." I pretended to be surprised. "Thank you for sending my picture in. Of course, I'll give you my Chargers gear if I win. I'm a Seahawks fan anyway. Kenny Easley and Walter Jones are my players."

Auntie Nhung let her husband off the hook with a disapproving look and said nothing. Hieu confessed next, but all he had was how he skimped on his chores by not spraying the tables down with Pledge cleaner. Instead, he used Pine-Sol. I gasped but Auntie Nhung was not amused. She went into a long soliloquy about why Pledge was best suited for the wood table because it was oil-free.

"It picks up all the dust while leaving a shiny luster." She compared the ingredients of Pledge and Pine-Sol and educated us on the chemicals in both products. "Pine-Sol is for degreasing and cleaning stubborn stains."

The woman even talked about how porous wood was compared to tiles. I was impressed with her knowledge of products and porous surfaces but equally annoyed with her rigid, duplicitous philosophy of what was proper and improper. How could a woman who ruled by fear instead of respect, who protected men's heinous acts of violence against women, and who manipulated the people around her, understand, much less educate others, on what was proper and improper?

I wondered what wrongdoing she would admit to that night. Maybe she would excuse herself from confession night because she was the queen and matriarch? Maybe it was an unspoken rule that she could do no wrong. I waited with bated breath.

"Amy, what do you have to confess?" Auntie Nhung asked.

"Oh," I said, "we haven't heard your confession yet. I'm going last, remember?"

Auntie Nhung dabbed the corners of her mouth with her napkin as if she were high society and proper. She folded the napkin and gently placed it across her lap. "I suppose it is my turn, isn't it?" She stalled a little by filling her glass of water to the top. She took a long sip and gently put the glass on the table. "Let me see."

I wondered if she would admit to slapping me. I didn't think she had told Dan about our kitchen feud where I threw the salt and pepper shakers at her, clawed at her throat, and bit her shoulder. Maybe it was because she lost that fight and didn't want to admit to losing to someone forty years her junior.

"Just admit it, Mom," Loc said. "You and Dad have sex all the time and you like it." Every jaw but Loc's dropped. Auntie Nhung's face turned crimson. "I hear you guys all the time, and you're always asking for more."

So Loc was not that innocent after all. He suddenly became my favorite. It took all my will power not to laugh. I shoveled food in my mouth like I hadn't eaten since the dawn of the Cenozoic Era. I kept my eyes down but my ears perked.

Auntie Nhung took another sip of water and dabbed her lips with her napkin. Dan broke the awkward silence by laughing. This embarrassed Auntie Nhung even more. She stood to clear the plates, even mine, though I was not done eating. I protested, saying I did not want to waste food, but she did not care.

Dan laughed so hard he triggered other emotions in his tiny hypothalamus. The tears leaked and he let out a fart. Loc and Hieu pointed at Dan and joined in the laughter. Without fail, flatulence always brought laughter, and the male species never seemed embarrassed. I giggled mainly because Dan was so nonchalant about passing gas at the table. All etiquette was out the window. We might as well have been laughing at Auntie Nhung, though, because she did not share the hilarity. She abhorred our juvenile behavior and feigned indifference.

The Yellow Jacket scooped up the salad bowl and grabbed Dan's plate. "Are you done?" He wasn't. She cleared the table anyway and put everything in the kitchen. "Lộc and Hiếu, load the dishwasher, and put the leftovers away."

We finished the night with a family movie called *Pretty Woman*. Auntie Nhung's mood changed as the night wore on. She let go of the embarrassment from earlier and dismissed the fact that both she and I got away with not spilling our beans. I was relieved because the only secret I had was Mama and Ace's visit while the family was out. I was not about to confess that and would have made up a story as absurd as Loc's and Hieu's.

The catfight between the two of us remained our little secret, and for the family's sake, we continued our charade. As far as everyone was concerned, my outburst at school and Auntie Nhung's scolding of my behavior was water under the bridge. I saw no reason to lift the veil and draw the curtains. The contempt lying beneath the surface remained concealed.

The Yellow Jacket and I moved forward with smiles and social graces. We behaved like mother and daughter instead of nemeses. Forty-five more days, I told myself. I had to survive long enough to finish my junior year of high school. Then I would be free of San Marcos High School, free of the Yellow Jacket, and free to be my true self.

15. THE MURPH (SPRING 1991)

A week before school got out, Dan handed me an envelope. It was from the Hire-A-Youth Program. I did not have high hopes. It was a statewide competition, and there must have been hundreds if not thousands of submissions. Dan shifted from foot to foot, but I stood motionless.

"C'mon, you can't leave me hanging," Dan said. "After all, I did send your entries in. I'm an accomplice now to your success."

"Entries?" I asked.

"Read it already, will you?"

I gently tore open the seal and took out the letter. I read it silently. I cocked my head to one side in confusion but a smile spread across my face as I continued reading. I frowned and scratched my forehead before handing the letter to Dan.

"Dear Amy," Dan read, "it is with great joy that we inform you of your placement in the statewide art and poetry competitions sponsored by the San Diego Chargers in partnership with Hire-A-Youth, a nonprofit organization that has been serving the young professionals of our nation since 1980. We received nearly three thousand submissions for both art and poetry contests. Your poetry submission of "Redemption" and your art entry of *Bliss* both placed in the top five in their respective categories. First, second, and third place winners will be announced at the annual televised Hire-A-Youth banquet on Saturday, June 15. Please join us for an evening of celebration. Poetry winners and honorable mentions will have the opportunity to read their poems at the dinner. You will meet potential employers, get inspired by our motivational speaker, and meet some of the San Diego Chargers players and cheerleaders. Please RSVP by May 30."

"I don't understand," I said. "My poetry submission never got sent in. I saw Auntie Nhung destroy it."

"So I have a confession," Dan said. "I took one of your crumpled versions of 'Redemption' and sent it off. I may have forged it and signed your name."

I opened my mouth to say thank you but closed them. Thanks weren't enough. My lips parted to try again, but I grasped for the right words to convey my sentiments. My eyes watered. Through all the endless days of darkness I had endured in San Marcos, Dan's light shone bright, yet he was content being in the shadows. No one had done anything so kind for me without any expectations in return. He genuinely believed in me and wanted me to succeed. I wrapped my arms around Dan and squeezed him with all my might.

"Thank you," I whispered. "Thank you for believing in me and truly seeing me, seeing my potential."

"You're a little songbird who has had her wings clipped," Dan said. "It's time you soar and sing again."

"Oh, Dan, what a poet you are," I said. "Are you sure you didn't write 'Redemption'?"

Dan gushed. "Want to check out the prizes?"

We sat down and poured over the details. Each nominee could bring two guests and pay extra for additional guests. The dinner would be held at "The Murph" with San Diego Charger's head coach, Dan Henning, giving the motivational speech. Prizes included a Chargers backpack full of football swag and autographed memorabilia, education credits toward art or writing classes at the local community college, a paid job placement for the summer, and tickets to NFL games. Other fun items like gift cards, trinkets, and interviews with the local TV channels were also included.

I called Mama and shared my good news. She shrieked and clapped her hands, saying she and Binh would come to the banquet. I told her I wanted only her to come but relented so that they could keep their façade of the happy couple. Dan sent in the RSVP letter and paid for his family of four to join me at the celebratory dinner.

The clouds finally gave way to a little sun haze. In two weeks, summer break would begin and so would my future. Mama would escort me up to Washington and get me settled into my new home in Aberdeen.

The Jack Murphy Stadium was transformed into a beautiful banquet hall under the cerulean sky. At one end of the field near the end zone was a large stage with a podium and projection screens all around. The band cranked out cover songs through the multi-million dollar audio-visual system. Cheerleaders walked around greeting the guests while television reporters pulled children and their parents aside to interview them. Waiters delivered trays of tapas and hors d'oeuvres and bartenders showed off their mixology talents by creating colorful cocktails. On the sidelines were photo booths and an 8'x8' step and repeat banner. The publicity backdrop had the San Diego Chargers lightning bolt logo and the Hire-A-Youth insignia. People were taking photos with the NFL players and cheerleaders and snapping photos in the booths.

Our group of seven found a round table at the fifty-yard line and settled in. We had one extra seat, and I wished Ace were there. Instead, he was on the naval station in Texas doing God only knew what.

"There are more people here than I expected," Auntie Nhung said.

I explained to her that there were subcategories within the art and poetry genres. Each subcategory had three placed winners and two honorable mentions. "In art, there's drawing, painting, photography, sculpting, carpentry, and mixed media. My stippling submission, Bliss, is under the drawing subcategory because it was done in ink."

"And here is your name under the poetry category," Mama exclaimed. "Our Vietnamese language is very poetic. It is good that you have poetry in your heart."

I looked at the program and saw the subcategories of haiku, ballad, free-verse, acrostic, sonnet, and epic. My "Redemption" poem was mentioned under acrostic. I explained to Mama that acrostic poems contain letters in each line that spell out a word or phrase. Typically, it is the first letter of each line that is used to spell out the message.

Arm in arm, I escorted Mama to the opposite sideline to the art display. The talent showcased on the field was impressive. The display included acrylics and watercolors, a piñata-looking sculpture of a big mouth titled *Speak Up*, and a photo within a photo within a few more photos that was titled *Reflections of Pain*. It reminded me of Bruce Lee's *Enter the Dragon* movie where he entered the hall of mirrors. The photo was in black and white, but the reflections of the girl in the red dress progressed from a vibrant scarlet to a dull raspberry. It spoke to me, and I understood the message. The pain never goes away. It will always be a part of us and makes us who we are, but in time, it gets diluted until it is not as bright and burning as in the beginning. We become different versions of ourselves in the healing process. I told Mama I bet *Reflections of Pain* would win first place in the photography subcategory.

"There is yours!" Mama squealed with excitement. "This my daughter drawing." She pointed to the 11x14 stippling portrait and bragged to anyone close enough to see my masterpiece. "My daughter, she draw that. That picture of me when I younger. Pretty then."

I didn't have the heart to tell her it was a portrait of an actress, so I let her believe it was her in her younger years when bliss lived in her heart.

We moved to the poetry section. Each framed entry rested on a stand. I pulled Mama to my poem. "I get to read this on the stage tonight in front of everyone. I'm so nervous."

"You should not be nervous," Mama said. "You are with winners. You should be nervous only if you had to read your last place poem next to the winning poem."

I laughed. "Way to put it in perspective, Mama."

She read one of the haiku poems and did not get it. "This is last place poem."

I giggled at her perspective and hoped the poet was not around to hear Mama. I had to admit I did not understand the underlying meaning within some of the poems but overall the verbal artistry was incredible and provocative.

By six o'clock, we all took our seats and enjoyed a four-course meal. Everyone was on their best behavior and dressed to impress in tropical casual attire. The fanciest thing I had was a mauve off-the-shoulder romper with a rose-colored velvet ribbon and nylon lace shawl.

Coach Dan Henning came to the stage and spoke about fighting for our dreams and that winners were not made overnight. He emphasized that we all were a part of the whole, a team, and to drive forward toward victory, every person had to do their part. He spoke about the fabric of our country was woven by the dreams of the young and shared success stories of players on his team who had big dreams. He reinforced how drive, perseverance, and a lot of stepping-stones would get us to where we aimed to go. He gave us a call to action to keep our eyes and ears open so that we might recognize opportunity, then keep our hands open so that we might seize the opportunity. When his motivational speech ended, I stood and applauded.

It was time for the award ceremony and one by one, poets climbed onto the stage to read the poem in their designated subcategories. Acrostic poems were read first. Coach Henning called my name. "Amy Le, reading her acrostic poem, 'Redemption.'"

I climbed the stairs and held my poem tightly, afraid it would blow away with the warm breeze. I stepped up to the microphone. "My poem is about living with shame but learning to fight back. It was written at a time when I felt I lost my voice."

*"**R**estless is the heart that cannot find.*
***E**roded in memory our joy that binds.*
***D**are I scrub away the shame?*

Evoked by you who scream and blame?
'Morrow the lark sings my name.
Petty and fear I play your game.
Tethered around the same Life pole.
I take back the me that you stole.
Over the clouds and rainbows, I rise.
Now and always, my warrior voice cries."

I finished my poem and listened to the delayed applause. Were people processing the poem, or did my poem suck? Either way, I was happy to get off the stage and listen to the other contestants read their poems. One girl stumbled over her reading, and it was painful to watch. She was anything but eloquent. Another boy read his poem, and he was so dramatic I imagined him on a theatrical stage performing a monologue.

Finally, the time came to announce the winners of the acrostic poetry subcategory. "Redemption" came in third place. My hands shook as I received my ribbon and basket of gifts. I stepped off the stage to take photos with the winners and ran back to my table. Loc helped me open the gift basket to see what was inside. I gave Loc the Chargers T-shirt and Hieu the hat. There were gift cards, chocolates, and a voucher for a free class at the community college. I gave the chocolates to Auntie Nhung and the college voucher to Dan. I had no use for those things. The gift cards to Target and K-Mart would come in handy.

The night continued and when it was time to announce the winners of the art contest, I sat at the edge of my seat and squeezed Mama's hands. When my name was not called in the drawing subcategory for third or second place, my heart sank. I would have to be happy with an honorable mention.

"And first place goes to…" Coach Dan Henning paused for effect. "Amy Le, *Bliss*."

I could not believe it. Had he called my name? Had I won first place? I cried with joy and walked slowly to Mr. Henning's outstretched hand. I placed my small hand into his and shook it firmly. The band played music and camera lights flashed in our direction. We smiled for the photographers, and Coach Henning slipped a large San Diego Charger backpack over my shoulders. He congratulated me and patted my shoulder as I strutted off the stage. I floated over the carpet and stood in front of the step and repeat banner to be interviewed by a reporter.

"Amy, you just won first place in the drawing category for your piece titled '*Bliss*.' Tell us about your work."

I beamed with pride for the camera. Adrenaline and endorphins raced through me. "It was done with a quill pen and ink. The technique is called stippling. Using thousands of dots, I created this picture of my mama. She was the inspiration." The words petered out, and I didn't care to correct myself. Yes, the portrait was of Michelle Yeoh, but the world did not need to know that. Perhaps subconsciously I chose this drawing and this model because she reminded me of Mama when she was young, carefree, and happy. It started as a portrait of an actress but it became a portrait of my hero, the greatest woman in my life.

I darted back to my table and took everything out of the backpack. Loc and Hieu oohed and aahed over my swag—everything from a signed football to tickets to a game. I pulled out a five-hundred-dollar gift card in an envelope, some art supplies, a rally towel, candy, and an offer of employment at an art studio for the summer. I gave Dan everything Chargers-related, including the backpack. He especially coveted the autographed football. I was sad to miss out on the summer job, but I couldn't wait to leave San Marcos.

I was ready for Seattle. Was Seattle ready for me?

16. GOODBYE CALIFORNIA (SUMMER 1991)

On the last day of school, I emptied my locker and dumped everything in the trash. Unloading the year lifted a great invisible weight off my shoulders. My backpack was light and so was my spirit. While others signed yearbooks, took pictures, and cried, I watched a few boys chase skirts, some girls swoon over their friends' summer plans, and teachers rush to the lounge as fast as humanly possible.

The brunette whose face I smashed earlier in the year lingered by the vending machine as she twirled her hair and flirted with a boy I recognized from my social studies class. They made a cute couple. Carina, Lily, Mary, and Phuong huddled together signing each other's yearbooks. My friendship with them was nice while it lasted, but I had no regrets that it ended. The relationship was superficial, and we each got what we wanted from it. They cheated off me and felt better about themselves while I masqueraded my loneliness and pathetic existence by being a part of something for a little while.

I waited under the eaves of the administration building at the front of the school for Loc and Hieu to meet me. Loc exited the double doors of the south building first. He spotted me and waved. He was his jovial self, full of mirth and animation. He wished everyone a great summer and stopped to sign yearbooks. For a goofy guy who loved zipper pants and British Knights high-tops, he sure was popular. His bucked teeth, receding hairline, and big glasses made him too adorable to be the target of bullying. Picking on Loc would have been like picking on a baby, and no one rallied around that.

Together we waited for Hieu and made small talk. Loc showed me a rose a girl gave him and gushed about her pretty eyes and teeth. He said she liked his muscles and then flexed them for me. I squeezed his arm and agreed they were bigger than at the start of school.

"What was your favorite class this year?" I asked. "Don't say PE."

Loc shyly looked away and smiled. "Home economics."

"Really?" I asked. "Let me guess. The girl who gave you that rose was in your home ec class." Loc didn't answer, and I knew I pinned the tail on the donkey.

Hieu finally shuffled out of the building. He was in no hurry to go home. He wore a lazy, relaxed smile when he saw us.

"Walk faster," I yelled.

He picked up his pace but still snailed along. I laughed and ran to him. I looped my arm through his and locked elbows. I dragged him to where Loc stood. Hieu ran with me but struggled to keep his bag on his back and his pants up.

"What was your favorite class this year?" I asked.

"Computing," he said. "Mr. Moss let me work on his new Windows 3.0 computer, and the user interface is rad. It's fast too. The CPU speed is fifty megahertz. I'm going to ask for a computer for Christmas, one that has at least four megabytes of RAM and two-hundred megabytes of hard disk space."

I laughed. None of his jargon made sense to me. "Come on, Brains. Come on, Brawns. I see your dad's car. Let's go home."

"Are you coming to my graduation?" Loc asked.

"Of course," I said. "I wouldn't miss it. You're going to look handsome walking across the stage to get your diploma."

Balloons and streamers adorned the house. Cupcakes, coconut rum banana bread, cream puffs, and lemon cheesecake filled the kitchen counter. A buffet of chafing dishes invited us to peek under the lids and drool over the fried rice, egg rolls, shrimp toast, chicken skewers, and sautéed garlic pea vines. The fragrances of ginger, garlic, onions, and coriander seduced me to grab a plate and serve up.

Auntie Nhung hugged each of us and presented us with a gift. Her kind gesture touched me. She congratulated us for surviving the year, then also congratulated herself and Dan for surviving. She puckered her lips and lifted them to Dan, who obliged and swooped down for a kiss. He handed her a glass of champagne and she eagerly accepted his offering. I had never seen her drink alcohol before.

It was indeed a day to celebrate. Loc was graduating from high school, I was leaving their home for good, and Hieu was the last one in the house for another year.

"Can I open my present?" Hieu asked.

Dan nodded. Hieu tore open the wrapping paper and rocked back and forth when he saw his Sega Genesis gaming console and Sonic the Hedgehog cartridge. His hands went from rubbing his head to covering his mouth. He leaped up and buried his head in his parents' shoulders.

"I love my present. Thank you so much."

"You can only play on Saturdays," Auntie Nhung said.

"My turn," Loc said. He ripped apart the wrapper and shrieked. He hugged his yellow waterproof Sony Walkman Sports cassette player like it was a puppy.

"It comes with headphones," Auntie Nhung said.

"And we got you a C+C Music Factory tape," Dan said.

Loc put the cassette tape into the home stereo equipment and surprised me by rapping the lyrics to the song *Gonna Make You Sweat*. He started to breakdance and cut the rug with his dance moves. Who knew?

"Go Loc!" I clapped. "Let's get this party started." He entertained us until Auntie Nhung stopped him.

"You're going to break something," she said. "It's called break dancing because people break their necks and hips...or TVs." She laughed at her joke. "Anyhow, it's Amy's turn to open her gift."

The lightweight, twelve-inch box in my hand had one simple blue ribbon tied around it. Long and thin, it could have held a plane ticket or a quill pen. I shook the box and smelled the cardboard, wondering if there were traces of chocolate or something sweet. I untied the ribbon and lifted the lid to find tissue paper. With great anticipation, I removed the top layer and stared at my gift. My fingers trembled as I lifted three crisp one-hundred-dollar bills out of the box.

I had never been so excited to see a famous, dead man's face. "Benjamin Franklin never looked more handsome."

Dan laughed.

I unfolded the note tucked inside the box and read it out loud. "Amy, this year went by fast, and despite the ups and downs, you've proven to us that you are one smart and determined young lady. We know you will go far, and we hope this gift will help you get there. Don't forget us."

"That should be enough to get you from Santa Ana to Seattle," Auntie Nhung said.

The tears gushed. "This is very generous." I felt guilty for causing them trouble. Perhaps I misjudged Auntie Nhung. Perhaps I was too headstrong and willful—too wrapped up in my pain to appreciate what she tried to do for me. In some ways, I was like the Yellow Jacket herself, struggling for power and control, but in trying to put my life back on track, I spun other people's lives off track.

Auntie Nhung opened her arms to me, and I conceded. I wrapped my arms around her waist and hugged her.

"I'm sorry for everything. I am grateful to you both. Thank you. You taught me structure and discipline and that anything worth doing needed to be done right. I see that now. I know I was a brat wrapped in my cocoon of hate."

"We all make mistakes," Auntie Nhung said. "It is easy to hate and punish others when we are unhappy with ourselves. And when good comes into our lives, we don't always accept it. We reject it, we lose hope, and in doing so, we drive others away, especially people who care about us because they are the closest and easiest to hurt. I know I am guilty of this, and I work at being a better person every day. I used to hurt Dan and my kids because I didn't think I deserved their love. I know I hurt you too. I did things in my past that I regret. They still haunt me, but I know I am not the same person I used to be. Circumstances can harden your heart and make you do things you know are wrong."

Dan picked up both of us into his big arms. "You both are so tiny. You're two halves of the same person." He laughed and bounced us up and down. I heaved from his jostling and made a hurling sound.

"I have been spiteful and said terrible things," I said. "I've lost control and been mean. If I did not have people who loved me and didn't give up on me, I think I would have continued down a very dark and lonely path of destruction."

"Don't waste your life," Auntie Nhung said. "Visualize what you want in life, and go for it, one step at a time. You'll get there."

"That's right," Dan said. "Enjoy the journey, because before you know it, you'll be an old fuddy-duddy like me."

The five of us continued the celebrations into the night. We gorged on food, listened to Loc's new cassette tape, and played Sonic the Hedgehog on Hieu's new Sega Genesis system.

I reflected on the year with Dan and Auntie Nhung and saw events from a different perspective. Auntie Nhung taught me that if I were going to do something, I needed to do it properly, whether it be cleaning the bathrooms or preparing for college. A wild wood tiger like me needed a strong handler like Auntie Nhung who had the backbone to be the bad guy. Had my stepdad not sent me away, I might have lost my virginity to Ace and gotten pregnant. I might have dropped out of school and branched off in a life of struggles and suffering. I might have fallen back with the Pomona Boys and served time behind bars.

Perhaps I needed to re-examine my relationship with my stepdad, but I didn't think I could forgive him for cheating on Mama. Was it even my place to forgive him? He needed Mama's forgiveness, not mine.

My mama once told me it was good to struggle when we are younger and face our demons early. Only then could we enter the second half of our life with eyes open and weapons in hand. I was still young—about to turn seventeen the following month. I knew there would be more challenges and suffering in my future before I entered the charming half of my life, but on that day, nothing else mattered. I had not felt such love, peace, and relief in a long time.

###

Mama and Binh came down for Loc's graduation ceremony and an early dinner. I watched with pride as Loc strode across the stage and received his diploma. The future was as bright as he wanted it to be. He planned to attend community college for two years and continue living with his parents, much to Dan's chagrin and Auntie Nhung's excitement. She teased that she had looked forward to having one less mouth to feed but secretly loved having both of her boys home for another year or two.

Having Mama there was the best gift of all. With the allowance I had saved and the three-hundred-dollar gift I received, I had enough money to buy both Mama and me a ticket to Seattle, with hers being round-trip so she could come back and finish her OMD training. We made plans while cooking together in the kitchen. Auntie Nhung, Mama, and I made curry chicken and braised beef stew. We sent Dan and Binh on an errand to pick up French baguettes, Mountain Dew, and Courvoisier.

Mama reminisced about the time I refused to eat curry and she sent me to bed hungry. "You were seven years old. I cannot believe that was ten years ago."

"I was so sick of curry," I said. "You made it all the time."

"That was the one dish I knew how to make well," Mama said.

"Yeah, and I remember the next day, that same bowl of cold curry waited for me at the table." I stuck out my tongue and wrinkled my face. "You forced me to eat every bite for breakfast. It was so gross."

"But you love it now and you never turn down food," Mama said. "I taught you well."

"That's because I know better," I said. "Imagine if I complained about fish soup or fried crepes. You would have made me eat cold fish eyes or soggy crepes and limp bean sprouts. Yuck."

By the time Dan and my stepdad returned from the stores, the food was ready to be served. Auntie Nhung cooked a pot of rice to go with the curry and we toasted the bread for the beef stew. Over dinner, we talked about lighthearted topics like Auntie Diep. Mama described her friend as unforgettable, like seeing a man in a thong. I chimed in about her bright outfits and said she probably escaped from the Oompa Loompa sanctuary. Mama scowled so I took back my comment and apologized.

"So Amy, do you know what you want to study when you get to college?" Dan asked.

"I'm thinking about journalism," I said. "I want to be a news reporter or have a talk show. I'm nervous about college though. My stepsister, Thu, told me to be prepared to work harder than a two-legged dog in an agility competition."

Hieu found that hilarious and could not stop laughing. "Or a one-legged man in a river dancing competition."

Dan and I burst at the seams. The visual brought me to tears, and I laughed until my sides ached. Loc put it in motion and demonstrated his river dancing skills with one leg. It was impossible to take him seriously. He bent down and substituted one of his legs with his arm and tried again.

"Ingenious," I cried.

"Almost as hard as my mom trying to parallel park," Loc said.

Auntie Nhung tugged at her son's ear. "Why are you always picking on me?"

"I only speak the truth, Mom." Loc blew her a kiss. "We all know you are short and have depth-perception issues."

My stepdad put his spoon down and grabbed a toothpick. He finished his meal first as usual. "Delicious."

"You're done?" Dan asked. "Did you even taste the food?"

Binh picked at his teeth. "I tasted every bite, and see? Here is proof." He dug out a piece of beef and showed it to us. I crinkled my nose and looked away. I still found his eating habits repulsive and unrefined.

Mama poured more Courvoisier XO into her glass and raised it for a toast. "To our children. May they make us proud and give us all their money."

Auntie Nhung nodded. "And cheers to us. I say we grab our OG panties and holster, granny up, and show these kids we're not hillbillies from Vietnam."

"What does that even mean?" I laughed.

"Now wait a minute," Dan said, "if yer gunna git yer panties, we menfolk are gittin our tobacca and rifle, too, cuz we can still show these youngins a thang er two!"

The adults tossed back their cognac and poured again. Loc, Hieu, and I shook our heads. They were getting a good buzz on, and by the end of the evening, they were loud, crude, and rambunctious. Binh brought out his guitar and strummed a melody while Auntie Nhung sang. Dan put on the karaoke system, and suddenly, we teenagers didn't exist. Mama and Auntie Nhung fought over who would sing next and debated whether Hương Lan or Ý Lan was the better singer. They channeled their inner Lans and sang a duet. The adults let loose and acted like teenagers. They sure did show us a thing or two.

###

My stepdad drove Mama and me to John Wayne Airport. Mama packed enough clothes for two weeks in Seattle. She would help me settle in my new home in Aberdeen, Washington, a small town located two hours' drive west of Seattle. We didn't talk on the way to the airport. Instead, each of us sat inside our heads, deep in thought, playing a movie reel of what the future had in store for us.

Binh was unusually quiet. He changed lanes often. He sped up then slowed down. He gripped the steering wheel until his knuckles turned white. I wondered if they fought earlier. I welcomed his silence. He still grated me the wrong way. I simply did not trust him. We had too much bad blood between us, but we tolerated each other for Mama's sake. In my memory, he was still the bad guy who monopolized Mama's time and persuaded her to leave a great job to move to California. He was the jerk who kicked my dog and gave her away. He violated my privacy and trust by reading my diary and barging into my room the day Ace was there. He packed my bags and sent me away to San Marcos. His threats about paralyzing me and confining me to a wheelchair still angered me.

My stepdad parked the car and removed our suitcases from the trunk. He still did not say a single word. Mama didn't seem to notice or care about the silent treatment. She was as excited as I to return to Seattle. I could not wait to get on the airplane and say, "Goodbye, California."

Mama talked about her childhood friend, Tien. They were like sisters growing up. Mama said her mother took Auntie Tien in and raised her for a few years. I hadn't heard that story before.

"Your grandmother raised Tien as her own and the two of us grew up as sisters," Mama said. "You will like her. She and her husband have five children. Her two youngest are around your age."

"Are they girls?" I asked.

"Boys," Mama said. "They have three boys and two girls. The oldest son is in the military, the oldest girl works for Boeing, and the next daughter is in college at Western Washington University. Todd is your age and will be in twelfth grade. You'll be going to Hoquiam High School together. The youngest is Thomas and he'll be entering ninth grade."

"What happened to Auntie Tien's parents?" I asked. "Did they die in the war?"

Mama shook her head. "They were poor and struggled to take care of their children and aging parents. Tien was not an orphan but in some ways she was. My mother loved her and took it upon herself to foster Tien. She is younger than me and very pretty. She was lucky. She married for love. It was not an arranged marriage. Her husband is a handsome and good man. He played soccer in Vietnam. You will like him. You are to address them as Auntie and Uncle Four."

The three of us went through security, and Binh escorted us to the gate. Mama and I gabbed about the foods we missed and how much we looked forward to seeing our friends. I wanted to drive by Homestead Apartments and visit Springbrook Elementary School for old times' sake.

"Who should we visit first?" I asked. "Is anyone picking us up at the airport? Where are we staying until we get to Aberdeen?"

Mama laughed. "So many questions. Uncle Skyler and Miss Magdaleine will pick us up at the airport. They will let me borrow their extra car while we are in town. I cannot wait to see my dear friends. We will stay with them for a week and then go to Aberdeen for a week."

I wished Mama could stay longer. I hated the idea of her returning to California and Binh. I reminded myself sacrifices were necessary. We had to stick to the plan.

Suddenly my stepdad knelt at Mama's feet and broke down in tears. I distanced myself from him and gripped Mama's hand.

"You are leaving me," Binh cried. "You have no plans to come back. I know you do not love me." He looked at Mama's face and begged her to stay. "I am sorry for hurting you. I know I can be a better husband. Please tell me there is still a chance."

Mama was speechless. She looked around at the bystanders watching the tragic scene unfold. She hushed my stepdad and tried to pull him to his feet. Mama's face reddened. I gawked at Binh.

He kissed Mama's feet and clung to her ankles, throwing her off balance. I clutched her arm to steady her. I had never seen a grown man cry. If I had empathy for him, I would have softened my heart and forgiven him that instant. Instead, I regarded his pleas and emotional outburst as pathetic. I wished I believed him. I wanted to think he could make my mama happy and not resort to his old ways. However, people did not change overnight. How many months or years must she endure before he changed? By then, it would be too late.

"You are embarrassing us and yourself," I said.

Binh ignored me. "Please, Snow, promise me you will come back. Remember our first trip to California, how we danced at the flea market? Remember our trip to Mt. Rainier when I proposed to you? Remember the first time we were together after Diệp and Donald's wedding? I made you happy once. Let me be that person again. You deserve that. I beg of you. Please forgive me, and give me another chance to make you happy. I promised to take care of you."

His appeals were working. Mama's face softened. "Yes, you did promise, but taking care of me meant also taking care of Thủy-Tiên. My daughter is a part of me, and after we moved down, you stopped taking care of her. It was as if you used her to get to me. I remember you showered us both with affection and gifts. You used to play with her and spend time with her. But then you treated her as a nuisance and a burden. I think you owe her an apology as well."

Binh and I looked at each other. His expression changed from vulnerable to stern. His body stiffened, and his posture became stoic. I tried not to gloat and wiped the smile from my face.

Binh stood up. I knew he was conflicted. I expected him to say he was the adult and that it was not his duty to apologize to a child. Would his arrogance get in the way of apologizing to me? Would he risk losing his wife out of stubborn pride and old patriarchal beliefs that the man was never wrong?

I held my breath and waited. I thought about making it easy on him by apologizing first, but I was obstinate also. We were at a standstill. Who was more pigheaded out of the three of us?

My stepdad took a deep breath. "You have not been the easiest child to manage—"

"I didn't need you to manage me," I said. "I needed you to be my friend."

"Do not interrupt," Mama said. "Let him finish."

My stepdad crossed his arms over his chest and widened his stance. "Look, you are off to the next stage of your life, and I wish you success. I know I put a lot of pressure on you to be perfect, and I admit I compared you to my daughter, Thu, and that was unfair of me. You are two different people. I forget that you grew up without a father and I tried too hard to be a father. I thought that was what you needed, maybe even what you wanted. I guess I came on too strong and too fast—"

"Yes," I said, "you did."

"Stop doing that," Mama said.

"Sorry," I said.

"Can we agree that becoming an instant family was all new to us?" my stepdad asked.

I nodded. "We were definitely out of sync and out of touch with one another."

Mama wrapped her arms around both of us. "We made decisions in silos, and we need to discuss them as a family."

"I know I am a child, and you were raised in a culture where men held the power and parents had all the authority, but here, they value independence. Children are contributors, and they have a seat at the table. They leave the nest and go off to pursue their dreams."

"But the American children also disrespect their elders, talk back to adults, and put their aging parents in nursing homes to rot alone," Mama said. "They do not discipline their children and they spoil them too much. We do not want you to become that way."

"Mama, I would never do that to you," I said. "Not all of us are bad. We act badly because that is what is expected of us before we're even given a chance. And I think it is prejudice to think American kids all behave that way."

"We have been in the United States for eleven years now," Mama said. "We are also citizens. I guess the real lesson begins now on adapting to Western society."

I smiled. "We may be Americans, but we're still Vietnamese. After all, my broken Vietnamese is still perfect."

Mama laughed. "Well, we tried. No one can blame us for trying to teach you how to read and write."

"On the positive side," my stepdad said, "her Spanish is good. We can take a vacation to Mexico, and she can be the interpreter."

"¡Sí Señor!" I said. "Yo hablo español muy bien. ¿Dónde está el baño? Mi cumpleaños es mañana. Por favor, dame cien dolares. ¿Cuanto cuesta el sombrero? Mucho gusto. ¿Como se dice 'vacation' en español?" I laughed as I rambled in Spanish to show off my language bravado. "Maybe I'll work for the FBI one day and be a translator, or work for border patrol and interrogate suspicious people."

An attendant for Alaska Airlines called for us to board. Mama and I collected our belongings and stood in line. My stepdad wrapped his arm around my shoulder and kissed me on the head. He never did say he was sorry, but neither did I. I let it go and knew in my heart I would never see him again. My mama had to decide what she was going to do. I had my future to focus on and to do that, I had to let go of the past.

The only thing I was not willing to let go of was Ace. I knew we would be reunited again after he got out of the Navy. Until then, my job was to graduate high school and get into college.

Mama and Binh kissed. I teased them about the public display of affection. Mama blushed and Binh told her to ignore me. They both chuckled and gave one last embrace before separating. We waved to Binh before entering the terminal. How sad he looked to be left behind.

Goodbye, California. Thanks for the new wave music and grunion run. Thanks for the Poison concert and my first kiss. Take care of my dog and save me a bowl of pho.

EPILOGUE

In 1991, Aberdeen, a small mill town in Grays Harbor County, had a population of 16,565 people. Once called "The Hellhole of the Pacific," the town was sprinkled with seedy whorehouses, saloons, and casinos. The murder rate was high and the timber industry boomed until the late 1970s. The logging by Weyerhauser had siphoned all the resources in the area. One pulp mill still operated, and the smell of vanilla permeated the town. Situated close to the Pacific Ocean, the overcast seasons were long and the rainfall heavy.

In that depressing town, the only Asian people I crossed paths with were Auntie and Uncle Four's family. Thomas, Todd, and I were the minorities at Hoquiam High School. If I were a bloodsucking vampire, Grays Harbor County would have been the perfect home. However, I had grown accustomed to the sunshine and beaches of California, so Aberdeen was a lonely and boring existence. There was nowhere a teen could go to find trouble.

Every day I went to school, then straight home to do homework. I spent most of my time in my bedroom and did not interact much with my host family. I felt like an intruder and did not want to impose or inconvenience them in any way. I helped Auntie Four in the kitchen every night as I was the only girl in the home.

Mama was right—Auntie Four was beautiful. She had aged gracefully over the years. I envied her long, thick black hair and bangs, her dimples, and the way she commanded love and respect from her husband and two sons. She was a strong woman on the inside, soft on the outside, and a great role model for me. She laughed a lot and had a young girl's spirit.

Auntie Four worked as a waitress in the only Chinese restaurant in Ocean Shores, a beach town twenty-five miles west of Aberdeen. I got a job at the Lucky Dragon restaurant and bussed tables for her on the weekends.

She split her tips with me, and I ate all the fortune cookies I wanted. The owner often fed us dinner before we drove home at night. I clutched the armrest as Auntie Four careened down dark, narrow, windy, two-lane roads. I imagined rolling down the cliff into the ocean. Auntie Four knew those roads like she knew the mannerisms of her children and always got us home safely.

Uncle Four used to work at the paper mill but was laid off. He loved watching soccer on TV and reminisced about the days in Vietnam when he played competitively. Uncle Four was handsome and fit. He had amazing legs and strong calves, a head full of hair, and a prominent jawline. He was quiet and reserved compared to Auntie Four. I don't think he knew what to do with me or how to act around me. I knew he loved me though from his small gestures of kindness, like giving me money just because or telling me about a scholarship I should apply to for free college tuition. Department of Social and Health Services had a dependent care program that provided cash assistance to families who needed help. We qualified and received four-hundred dollars each month. Uncle Four gave me three-hundred dollars each month and kept only a hundred to cover my room and board. By the end of my senior year, I had saved three-thousand dollars in my shoebox under the bed. I had no friends, no need for shopping, and no urgent expenses. I bought milkshakes or small gifts for the family during the holidays and birthdays with the money I made bussing tables at the Lucky Dragon.

I coasted through my senior year and graduated with honors. I was friendly with my classmates and got along nicely with Todd and Thomas, but never developed lifelong friendships or deep connections in Aberdeen, Hoquiam, and Ocean Shores. When I considered my university options, I decided I would go either to Western Washington University (WWU) or Washington State University (WSU), the two schools farthest away from Aberdeen but still within the state. WSU was a party school whereas WWU was close to the Canadian border, and the legal drinking age in Canada was nineteen. I chose WWU because Auntie Four's children went there, and Todd also got accepted to the university. Not to mention I won a scholarship to WWU and my first year was free.

Mama flew up, and together with Auntie and Uncle Four, we drove to Bellingham and settled into our dorms. It was a beautiful campus with grand brick buildings and a large water fountain in the center courtyard. The school was nestled in a charming coastal town with hiking trails and lakes on one side and beaches and scenic drives on the other. My four years there were the best years of my life. Dorm life and cafeteria food did not agree with me though. After one quarter, I wrote a letter to the board requesting a release of obligation from my residential contract, stating that the food didn't agree with me, and the loud parties obstructed my educational endeavors.

My roommate, Rina, was Cambodian and sad to see me go. She and I bonded and were inseparable. I often went home with her to Tacoma to visit her family and stock up on home-cooked meals. I missed authentic Asian foods and realized how much it defined me as a Vietnamese girl growing up in an American world. When I moved out of the dorm, I met Jane, my first Korean friend, who introduced me to bulgogi, onion pancakes, and kimchee. My housemates and I rented a townhome near campus and lived in the same complex as Todd and his roommates. James and Carrie were my roommates. I rarely saw James. He was a very tall black man with beautiful eyes and had served in the Marine Corp. He was working on an engineering degree. Carrie was a party animal, always late on her share of the rent, and the epitome of the ditzy blonde stereotype. We all stayed out of each other's way and circulated with peers who never hung out together.

I joined the Vietnamese Student Association (VSA) and found like-minded friends who loved potlucks and karaoke. Several times a week, we gathered for study sessions that turned into one hour of studying and two hours of eating and socializing. We ran the VSA club together, formed a volleyball team, and took trips to Vancouver, British Columbia, to eat and dance at the nightclubs. Richard's on Richards was our favorite night raver hotspot to flirt and lose our body to the beats of hip hop. College was a defining event in my life where I developed my political views and grew into my skin.

Mama and I spoke every Sunday morning and if I didn't call, she worried and gave me a lecture. Her life unraveled, and she took a break from school. Life with my stepdad was good for a while, but he continued to squander money. Mama said he was addicted to sex, something I didn't want to hear, and that he found attention elsewhere. She was miserable but she could not leave him yet. I encouraged her to get a financial loan to continue school, get a job, and move out. I offered to buy her a ticket to Seattle, but she was adamant that I focus on school. She would figure things out.

I had a job under a work-study program at Disabled Students Services and got paid to read textbooks into a cassette recorder for the visually impaired students. I also worked at Payless Shoe Source and while I was the top salesgirl each month, I admittedly spent my paychecks on shoes. I got a credit card and with my newfound freedom, I spent all my money shopping, eating out, partying, and buying books.

One sunny autumn day, I bundled up in my turtleneck sweater and knitted cap and took a walk outside to enjoy the beauty of the fall leaves on display. Washington had the best deciduous trees with foliage that turned from green to tones of gold, vermilion, amber, and apricot in late October. I checked the mailbox to see if there was anything fun. On occasion, James received letters from home, and Carrie received checks from her grandparents. All I ever got were junk mail, bills, and letters from Ed McMahon tempting me to join the Publishers Clearing House for a chance to win cash and prizes.

My breathing stopped and my heart skipped a beat when I recognized the handwriting on an envelope with a postmark from Oklahoma. I tore it open and caught a whiff of Ace's Obsession cologne. I put the letter to my nose and inhaled the scent. Tears of joy ran down my cheeks as I stood beneath the maple trees savoring the scent of his cologne and the romantic curves of his writing. My heart pounded. Was it bad news? I sat down on the viridian moss and counted the pages. Five. I turned straight to the end to see if he included a phone number. He had—one with a 405 area code.

He got out of the Navy in April 1993 and met a girl online named Trâm. He sold his Supra to his brother and moved to Oklahoma City in May. He bought a Nissan Maxima and was slowly modifying it, dropping the car to the ground, putting on low-profile tires, installing lights under the chassis, tinting the window, and putting on a new spoiler. In the fall, he started school at Oklahoma State University (OSU). He never stopped loving me and never stopped thinking of me. He thought all was lost, but then he found Marina's address and wrote to her. She wrote back and gave him my address in Bellingham. He was sure I had moved on, but if I still loved him, he would drop everything and come to me.

I read the letter a second time before I rushed to the townhouse and picked up the phone. My heart fluttered with excitement. Hearing from Ace was better than winning a Publishers Clearing House prize. I had dreamed of this day, and soon I would hear his voice. Two long years I had waited. I had so much to tell him and catch up on. With trembling hands, I made the long-distance phone call from my bedroom on my cheap, lip-shaped telephone that I purchased at Spencer's next to Payless Shoes Source at Bellis Fair Mall.

"Hello?" A girl answered.

"Hi," I said. "Can I talk to Ace?"

"Who's this?" she asked.

I wasn't sure whether to say Amy or Christine so I answered, "An old friend." She was quiet. I thought the call got disconnected. "Hello?"

"I'm still here," she said. "Is this Christine?"

I fumbled the phone and almost dropped the receiver. She knew who I was. "Anh Bé has talked about you." Who the hell was Anh Bé? "This is Trâm, his girlfriend."

"He mentioned you in his letter," I said. "Can I talk to him? Is he home?"

"No, he's not home," she said coldly. "He's at the restaurant helping my dad and learning the family business."

"Well, what time will he be home?" I asked. "I'll call back."

"No, you won't." Tram told me they had been dating for six months, that she loved Ace and was not giving him up without a fight. She said he had started school at OSU and needed to focus on his education. "We are happy together. If you want him to be happy and not distract him from his studies, I suggest you forget him and never call back." Apparently, all Ace ever talked about was me, his first love, his old flame, and the regrets he had. "I am tired of hearing about you, and I don't have the patience any longer to entertain his fantasies of reuniting with you." She hung up on me.

Oklahoma City was two hours ahead of Bellingham. I debated whether to call later that night but knew Tram would be monitoring the phone. I didn't call back that night or the following night.

On the third night, I could not take it anymore and resolved to talk to Ace. Tram was not going to dissuade me so easily. I dialed the number and the phone rang four times.

"Hello?"

My heart hammered inside my chest and somersaulted into my throat. It was my Ace.

"Christine, is that you?"

I nodded but could not speak. Finally, I whispered, "Yes."

"Oh honey," Ace said. "Oh baby, I can't believe I'm talking to you right now. Tram told me you called and we had a big fight. I was afraid she scared you off and you wouldn't call again. I threatened to drive to Washington if she pulled that again."

"Is she home?" I asked.

Ace laughed. "Yes, she's here next to me and planning my murder."

I had no ill feelings toward Tram. I empathized with her. I knew what it felt like to love Ace and how amazing it was to be loved by him. She was in a difficult situation. I was the ghost from the past that haunted them both.

"Well tell her I am back, and I'm reclaiming what I lost. You were mine long before you were hers."

Ace and I spoke for twelve hours straight. We had so much to say, and neither one of us wanted to hang up. We made plans for him to fly out and visit me after Christmas when the airfare was cheaper. We had waited for two years and would have to wait two more months. I came alive as I told him all about my life in San Marcos and Aberdeen. He talked about life in the

Navy and how his younger brother married a redhead in Texas. Ace asked me if I had dated anyone after him, and I told him I had dated a college boy from Lopez Island but it did not last long. The islander boyfriend wanted to get married and move to Hawaii so he could be a geologist. I wasn't uprooting again and leaving Washington. Ace and I had a good laugh when I told him the ex-boyfriend stole all my seasonings during the breakup.

Ace and I finally hung up at six in the morning. I slept the entire day and woke up happier than ever.

###

I took the Greyhound bus down to Seattle and met Ace at the airport. The moment he stepped out from the tunnel, I jumped into his arms and kissed him fiercely. He looked the same except with longer hair. We held each other with my head buried in his chest for a long time. The moment was surreal. I did not let go for fear he'd vanish into thin air. We kissed and hugged, and just like in the movies, it felt like the world moved on without us. Time stood still. People came and went. Planes landed and took off. We didn't speak.

We pried ourselves apart and headed to baggage claim. Every few steps, we stopped and kissed again. It took us twice as long to get to the lower level to collect his suitcase. I didn't have a car and told him we'd have to take the Greyhound back to Bellingham. I took the bus everywhere and learned the route to get to work. If I needed groceries, I walked the mile down to Haggen and then back up the long hill with my bags of food. It was good exercise but exhausting.

"My poor baby," Ace said. "Let's find you a car while I'm here, something cheap for under a thousand dollars."

"How long are you here for?" I asked.

"Two weeks," he answered. "And I was thinking, if you want, I could apply to transfer to Western. If they accept me, which they will, I'll move here in June."

"And we can start school together in the fall!" I hopped like a bunny and squeezed his hand. "We can find our own place or maybe Carrie or James will move out by then."

We pulled Ace's luggage off the conveyor belt and took a taxi to a nearby hotel for the night. It was too late to catch a bus back to Western. Inside our hotel room, Ace and I cuddled and talked until our stomachs growled. We grabbed food at a diner and brought it back to the room. We started a movie and ate but soon abandoned the movie.

Ace looked at me with tenderness and desire in his eyes, and I knew it would be the best night of our lives. He turned off the light and opened the curtain a sliver to let the moonlight witness our lovemaking. I removed my clothes and helped him remove his. We stood naked. I traced his curves and lines with my eyes. His silky skin warmed my fingertips. I hungered for him, but he took his time and drove me crazy.

He flipped me over onto my stomach and gave me a massage with his lips and tongue. His touch fluttered from my neck down to the small of my back like a butterfly leaping from flower to flower. His hardness pressed against my legs, and I parted them slightly.

"Not yet," he whispered.

His tongue circled my earlobes as his hand found its way to my breasts and inner thighs. My body throbbed for him. I rolled onto my back and looked into his eyes just inches from mine, and I inhaled as he exhaled. One breath. One heartbeat. One body.

He caressed me and murmured he wanted to explore every inch of me. He mapped out my body with his eyes and lips, and the temptation was too much to bear. My body tingled under his light touch. His hair tickled my stomach when he moved down past my hips to the folds of my femininity. And when his hot breath landed on the pearl between my legs, I gasped. My toes curled and my body tensed. I shook and orgasmed for the first time. I dug my nails into his shoulders and pulled his head closer. His tongue enjoyed torturing me, and when his mouth found mine again, I took pleasure in returning the favor.

Ace and I made love for hours, releasing years of pent-up frustration, separation, and longing.

Ace bought me a white 1985 Honda Civic, four-speed manual transmission, for nine-hundred dollars. The base model hatchback had a solid engine and got me where I needed to go but not very fast. In the summer, he drove his Nissan from Oklahoma City to Bellingham and started school in the fall at WWU. Carrie and James did not move out, so we split the rent four ways with Ace and me taking over the master bedroom. Ace joined the VSA and life resumed with potlucks, karaoke, and trips to Vancouver.

We stayed together for four years. Ace got the sales engineer position at IBM and quickly received a promotion. He wore suits to work and took long trips to Amsterdam and other exotic places. Over time, we drifted apart. He worked a lot and spent more and more time at the casinos to decompress. On the night I planned to give him an ultimatum, I prepared a romantic evening picnic in our bedroom with candlelight and wine. I drew him a card and wrote him a poem. I turned on the music, slipped on a sexy black dress, and waited. Hour after hour, I ran to the bedroom window to see if the headlights belonged to the Maxima. It was never him. I drank the bottle of wine in under an hour and got drunk for the first time. The walls tilted, and the room spun. I laid down to rest my eyes and thought about our breakup.

Ace found me passed out on the bed, lying rigid on the mattress with my hands clasped on my stomach like a dead person. He cried, panicked that I had alcohol poisoning. He rubbed lemon juice on my palms and the bottoms of my feet—a superstitious belief that the citrus would absorb into my bloodstream and release the toxins. We did not break up that night but our relationship changed.

He hurt me deeply, but I loved him enough to part as friends after all we had been through. As our hearts healed, we became best friends and could laugh again. Ace left Washington, and I bought the Supra from his brother as a memento of our life together. I paid Tung to drop the transmission and put in a manual stick shift. I covered his travel expenses, and two months after Ace left Washington, the Supra arrived at my doorstep—the perfect part of Ace to keep close to my heart.

Ace and I kept in touch and dated other people. While there was some jealousy underneath our cool demeanors, we never interfered in each other's love lives. Ace dated a gal named Anna who was intimidated by me and insecure in her relationship with Ace. She was smart, nice, and came from a rich family. She was also plain looking with a big forehead and weak chin. It made me uncomfortable to watch her fuss over him. When I started dating Charlie, Ace admitted he wanted to smash Charlie's head into the window. He found Charlie too arrogant and thought he was a player.

The years passed and President Bill Clinton came into office. He appointed Ruth Bader Ginsburg to the Supreme Court as the second female Justice to hold that seat, and in 1994, he lifted a nineteen-year-old trade embargo with Vietnam. A year later, Mama got her OMD in acupuncture. She left Binh and never looked back. Mama was a fan of President Clinton until the extra-marital affair scandal came to light. She lost all respect for him so when I met him a decade later and told her I shook his hand, she asked me if his hands were dirty. I told her it was soft like butter with no callouses.

Mama found a small apartment in downtown Seattle on First Avenue and walked across Post Alley to get to the Pike Place Market every day for fresh seafood, meats, fruits, and vegetables. She adopted a black toy poodle and named her Bijoux. The two doted on each other and loved one another unconditionally. Mama and Bijoux took walks every day, and the vendors at the market knew them by name.

Once again Mama and I lived our best lives in Seattle with no drama or baggage to hold us back. Our most cherished moments were in the kitchen when I helped Mama prep and she cooked. We laughed over her mispronunciation of ingredients or clever renaming of cuisines. For example, sushi came to be called *xù xì* which meant shaggy, and cassoulet was "cá so lazy," which made no sense because *cá* meant fish. Fish so lazy was far from what the French coined a meat casserole.

In 2000, President Clinton visited Vietnam—the first president to travel there since the war. Mama and I held our breath as we tuned into the news to understand what his visit meant for us going back home and seeing our family. Another eight years passed before Mama, Tree, and I reunited with our mother country.

In between those years, I met a man I married but divorced after two years of abuse. Tree moved his family back to Seattle, and once again, we were together in the city that had welcomed us with open arms when we were poor refugees who knew nothing about life in a free nation.

By 2008, I worked for a great company called Microsoft, took home a six-figure income, owned two cars, paid off my student loans, and answered to no one. I had been dating a man ten years younger than me and married him that year. My father came to the wedding. Mama and my dad reconnected after she left Binh and returned to Seattle. He came to visit a few times, but I was too busy with work and travel to spend any time with him. Subsequently, I regarded him as an old friend from out of town who occasionally visited.

Nearly thirty years after escaping the clutches of communism on a rickety old shrimp trawler, Mama, Tree, and I flew home to our roots. Mama and her siblings picked up right where they left off in 1979, with tears of pain but hope for a brighter future. How sweet it was to get to know my aunties and uncles, to meet my cousins, and dote on their children. The family house still stood and continued to raise another generation of children.

I had left Vietnam a sick, frail child with an uncertain future and came back a healthy woman living the charmed life I dreamed of for myself. Mama and Tree were happy, healthy, and reaping the rewards that America afforded them. We spent a month in Vietnam getting reacquainted with the land, the people, the foods, and the traditions. I left there humbled, enriched, and fluent enough to think and dream in Vietnamese.

Ace later reunited with his parents in Vietnam and built them the house he promised. Mama and I never saw Binh again and Mama remained single until the day she passed. She lived life on her terms. Mr. and Mrs. Vanzwol retired to Arizona and the rest of our friends and family continued the rat race of living. We came full circle. We faced our fears, pushed through the pain, and found happiness within the strong bonds of love, forgiveness, and family.

Despite our busy lives, we made time for family. Food brought us together around Mama's kitchen or the family table. Tree's children and my son were the second generation to gather in the kitchen and feast on traditional dishes, such as braised catfish and spring rolls. We are now at generation 3.0. I hope our family will always remember the sacrifices of those before us and that our stories live on in the foods prepared in the kitchen and presented at the table.

To eat is to survive, but to cook is to live.

THE END

In memory of Snow

Tree, Snow, and Dolly – Vietnam 2008

Ace and Christine

Christine and Van

Amy Chen, a friend, and Christine at Asian Garden Mall

Vietnamese Student Association – Western Washington University
(Amy aka Christine aka Dolly is in the center, red áo dài)

Dolly at the ceramic shop with dog Nikki
and the haircut that made her cry.

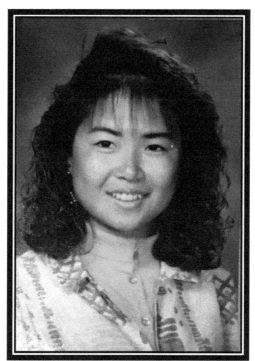

Amy Chen

Ace and Amy (aka Christine) in college

Ace and Amy (aka Christine) in college

Amy and Snow on the first day at WWU campus
(Aunt and Uncle Four in the background with their van)

Amy graduated from Hoquiam High School with honors

Snow graduated with OMD in acupuncture

Amy and Snow at a temple in Seattle,
dressed as queen and king

Dolly and Snow (August 2016)

SNOW'S KITCHEN
A COOKBOOK

Contents

APPETIZERS & SIDES

Bánh Bao (Steamed Pork Buns)

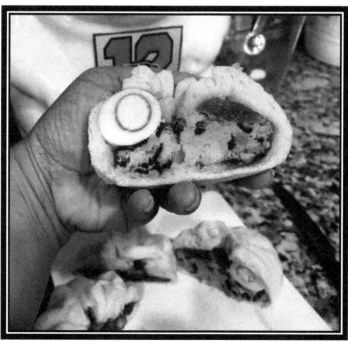

Ingredients:

Dough:
1-16 ounce package Bột Bánh Bao (Steamed Dumpling Bun Flour)
*Follow the instructions on the package. You will need about 1/3 cup of sugar and water or milk to prepare the dough according to the package.

Filling:
1.5 lbs ground pork
½ small sweet yellow onion (peeled & chopped)
½ cup dried wood ear mushrooms (softened in hot water, drained, then chopped)
1 Chinese sausage (sliced thin diagonally into 10 pieces)
10+ quail eggs (hardboiled for 10 minutes, peeled)
*Substitute 2-3 hardboiled chicken eggs if you do not have quail eggs. Cut each hardboiled egg into 3-4 wedges, enough for ten baos.

Marinade:
2 tablespoons oyster sauce
½ teaspoon sugar
½ teaspoon salt
¼ teaspoon ground black pepper

Other:
Steamer or a pot with a lid and flat-bottomed colander
Sheets of printer paper, cut into 10 circles, each about 3 inches wide
¼ cup flour for dusting the rolling pin and countertop
*If you do not have a rolling pin, use a highball drinking glass to roll the dough. Whatever you do, don't use your beer can. Party foul. That's for drinking, not rolling.

Directions:
1. Follow the instructions on the banh bao flour package and separate the dough into 10 equal balls, because seriously, who has time to make the dough from scratch?
2. Soak the wood ear mushrooms in a bowl of very hot water for 15 minutes. I like my water at 195 degrees F but you can eyeball it. (Kidding, don't stick your eyes into hot water.)
3. Drain and rinse the mushrooms, then chop into small pieces.
4. In a large bowl, combine ground pork, wood ear mushrooms, and chopped sweet yellow onions.

5. In a small bowl, mix the oyster sauce, sugar, salt, and black pepper. Taste the marinade and add more salt or sugar to your liking. (Now would be a good time to sip your wine or feel-good juice.)
6. Pour the marinade into the pork mixture and combine well. Separate the filling into 10 equal-sized balls.
7. Dust the countertop and rolling pin with flour. Roll each dough ball into a 4-inch circle.
8. For each dough circle, place pork, egg, and a slice of Chinese sausage in the center.
9. Gather up the edges of the dough to wrap the filling and twist the center point to seal the banh bao.
10. Place the banh bao onto a pre-cut sheet of paper.
11. Steam the banh bao in batches for 15-20 minutes. (This is a good time to have more wine.) If you do not have a steamer, bring a large pot of water to a boil. Place the baos in a flat colander and nestle it in a pot of water. Make sure the bottom of the colander is not sitting in water. Steam with the lid on.
12. The banh bao will almost double in size so do not crowd the steamer.
13. Carefully remove the baos and let them cool for a few minutes before eating. You must close your eyes when you eat these, so you don't see the calories or carbs you're consuming.
14. Wrap extra baos in plastic wrap and store in the fridge. When you're hankering for a bao, warm one up in the microwave or steamer.

Bánh Bèo (Steamed Rice Cakes)

Ingredients:

Dough:
1-12 ounce package Bột Bánh Bèo (Banh Beo Flour)

Toppings:
½ cup dried mung beans (soaked overnight then steamed until soft)
¼ cup dried shrimp (soaked in 2 cups hot water for 30 minutes, drain)
1 pound shrimp (deveined, chopped into small pieces without the shell)
½ pound pork belly (discard the skin & cut the pork into small pieces)
4 cloves garlic (minced)
4 shallots (minced)
½ cup green onions (chopped)
As needed: vegetable oil or bacon grease

Garnishes:
½ cup green onions (chopped)
¼ cup fried shallots/onions

Other:
10 ramekins or 15+ small ceramic saucers
Steamer or a pot with a lid and flat-bottomed colander
Pestle and mortar or food processor
Slotted spoon or ladle

Sweet Chili Fish Sauce:
¼ cup fish sauce
¾ cup coconut soda or water
¼ cup sugar
2 tablespoons lime juice
1 red chili pepper (minced) or 1 tablespoon chili sauce

Combine all the sauce ingredients into a bowl and mix. Taste the sweet chili fish sauce. It should be a balance between sweet and tangy. Add more sugar, fish sauce, or coconut soda if needed until the sauce reaches the flavor you desire.

Remember this recipe. Trust me, it's at the top of the V-ADED (Viet-All Day Ev'ry Day) food pyramid and a staple in Snow's Kitchen.

Directions:

1. STOP! Ask yourself. "Do I love them enough to make this for them?" This is a labor of love and if you answered no, find something else to make. If you answered yes, proceed.
2. Make sure you soak the dried mung beans overnight before starting.
3. Soak the dried shrimp in 2 cups of hot water for 30 minutes, then drain and grind up the dried shrimp in a food processor or with a pestle and mortar. Set aside in a bowl.
4. Drain and rinse the soaked mung beans then steam them until soft, about 20 minutes.
5. While the mung beans are in the steamer, prepare the sweet chili fish sauce by combining all the sauce ingredients into a bowl and mix.
6. Taste the sweet chili fish sauce. It should be a balance between sweet and tangy. Add more sugar, fish sauce, or coconut soda if needed until the sauce reaches the flavor you desire.
7. Ground the mung beans into a paste using a pestle and mortar or food processor. Set aside.
8. In a pan over medium-high heat, add a tablespoon of oil and stir-fry the pork belly pieces to render the fat.
9. Add minced garlic, minced shallots, and both dried and raw shrimp.
10. Stir-fry the shrimp and pork until both are cooked. Add additional vegetable oil or bacon fat if the pork belly does not render enough fat to fry the shrimp, onions, and garlic.
11. Add the ½ cup chopped green onions and mix well.
12. Using a slotted spoon or ladle remove the filling and set it aside in a bowl. You want the filling dry and crispy not oily and soggy.
13. Add the remainder of the green onions and shallots to the pan and fry in the greased pan for your garnish.
14. Prepare the steamed rice cakes according to the banh beo package. You will need to steam the cakes in batches.
15. Remove the steamed rice cakes and top each one with the shrimp and pork mixture. Sprinkle fried green onions and scallions on top to garnish.
16. Spoon the sweet chili fish sauce over the rice cakes and enjoy.
17. Reevaluate whether the people you fed these to are worthy of your efforts. If not, give them "MustGo" meals i.e. three-day-old leftovers in the fridge that must go, or else they'll go on their own.

Chả Giò (Egg Rolls)

Ingredients:

Wrappers:
1 package of egg roll wrappers (Each package comes with 25 sheets and can be found in the frozen section of most Asian grocery stores. Defrost for 15 minutes then ask your child to peel each wrapper into separate sheets.)
2 egg yolks, lightly beaten (Keep the whites for the filling.)

Filling:
1 pound lean ground pork or ground chicken
1 pound shrimp (peeled, deveined, lightly ground in a food processor)
(Substitute the meat and shrimp with fried tofu or portabella mushrooms for an alternative option.)
1 cup cabbage (chopped in a food processor)
1 cup carrots (chopped in a food processor)
Optional: 1 cup daikon (chopped in a food processor)
1 cup dried wood ear mushrooms or fresh mushrooms (soak the dried wood ear mushrooms in hot water for 15 minutes, then drain, and chop in a food processor)
2 egg whites
2 tablespoons pre-made sweet chili fish sauce (See page 137)
2 tablespoons granulated chicken flavor soup base mix (bouillon)
1 teaspoon ground black pepper
1 teaspoon salt

Dipping Sauces (optional to your preference):
pre-made sweet chili fish sauce or thick sweet chili dipping sauce
*To make your own sweet chili fish sauce, see the sauce ingredients for the Bánh Bèo (Steamed Rice Cakes) on page 137.

Oil:
peanut oil, avocado oil, sunflower oil, or any oil with a high smoke point. (You will need enough to fill a pot or pan 2 inches of oil to fry the egg rolls.)

Other:
silicone brush
food processor
paper towels

*Serve egg rolls with vermicelli noodles, other meats, veggies, and herbs for a nice meal. Be sure to drizzle sweet chili fish sauce on the noodles!

Directions:

1. In a large bowl, combine all the filling ingredients EXCEPT the egg yolks. Set the yolks (not to be confused with yokes) aside in a small bowl.
2. Use your hands to mix the ingredients well, unless you're bougie and prefer a wooden spoon or spatula. My bougie meter depends on the length of my fingernails at the time of making these.
3. Place one egg roll wrapper on a plate and position the wrapper so that a corner is pointed at you in a diamond shape.
4. Spoon two tablespoons of the filling onto a sheet of egg roll wrapper an inch from the closest corner to you. Spread the filling out so it is two inches long, horizontally.
5. Roll the wrapper around the filling firmly by taking the corner closest to you and cover the filling. Roll and tuck the wrapper nice and tight to minimize air pockets.
6. Fold the side corners into the middle and continue rolling until you have an inch left at the end.
7. Use a silicone brush to moisten the end corner of the wrapper with a touch of the slightly beaten egg yolk wash. This will seal the egg roll. Use your finger if you're feeling like a Neanderthal.
8. It is super important you sip wine after each roll to celebrate your amazing accomplishment. After all the egg rolls have been rolled, you can fry them or freeze them in a plastic bag for later.
9. When you are ready to fry the egg rolls, heat the oil on medium heat in a pan or pot. The oil level should be two inches.
10. Once the oil is hot, fry the egg rolls in batches for 6-8 minutes until golden brown. Remove the egg rolls and let them rest on a plate lined with paper towels to soak up the excess oil.
11. Enjoy the egg rolls plain, with your choice of dipping sauces, or in a vermicelli noodle bowl with vegetables and herbs.

Chả Trứng (Egg Meatloaf)

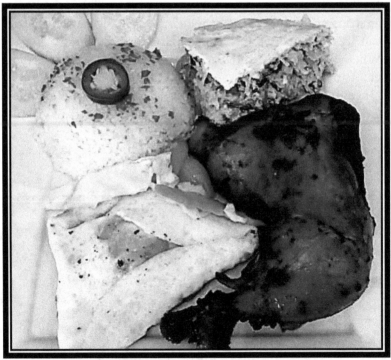

Ingredients:

½ cup dried wood ear mushrooms (soaked in hot water for 15 minutes, then drained and chopped)
1 pound ground pork
½ pound shrimp (remove the shell, devein, and chop in a food processor)
5 eggs (separate the yolks and whites)
4 shallots (minced)
1 carrot (chopped in a food processor)
3 cloves garlic (minced)
1 cup mung bean thread noodles (soaked in hot water for 15 minutes, then drained and cut into 1-inch pieces)
2 tablespoons fish sauce
1 tablespoon sugar
1 teaspoon salt
1 teaspoon ground black pepper

Other:
steamer or pot with a lid and flat-bottomed colander
parchment paper
silicone spatula
sweet chili fish sauce (See page 137)

Directions:
1. In a large bowl, mix all of the ingredients EXCEPT FOR <u>four</u> of the egg yolks.
2. Line a flat cake pan or deep plate with parchment paper – anything that will fit in the steamer.
3. Spread the meat evenly into the pan and smooth out the top surface.
4. Whisk the 4 egg yolks and pour them evenly over the meatloaf. Use a silicone spatula to spread the yolk so it covers all of the meat.
5. Place the meatloaf in a steamer. Cover and steam for 20 minutes.
6. Remove the lid making sure to not let the condensation drip onto the meatloaf. If you do, it's okay, just don't tell anyone.
7. Remove the steamed egg meatloaf and let it cool for 10 minutes before slicing into it.
8. Serve the meatloaf as a side to accompany rice and other meats and vegetables.
9. For extra flavor, drizzle sweet chili fish sauce on top. To make your own sweet chili fish sauce, refer to the sauce ingredients on page 137 under the Bánh Bèo (Steamed Rice Cakes) recipe.

Charcuterie Board

The possibilities are endless for this appetizer. Here are our favorites.

Ingredients:

Cheeses:
soft cheeses: triple cream brie, camembert, Couer de Chevre, Neufchatel
hard cheese: BellaVitano merlot, smoked gouda, cheddar, gruyere, manchego

Meats:
Peppered salami, pastrami, smoked salmon, pâté de foie gras, sausage

Nuts:
Cashews, macadamia, pistachios

Fruits:
champagne mangoes, kiwis, raspberries, blueberries, blackberries,
strawberries, pineapples, persimmons, jackfruit, pears, mangosteens,
pomegranates, apricots, figs, papayas, plums, sugar apples, lychees, grapes

Dips and Spreads:
hummus, garlic herb cream cheese, blackberry jam, cranberry orange relish,
spinach and artichoke dip, pesto, avocado, orange marmalade, bruschetta,
salmon dip

Crackers/Bread:
Kii Naturals Artisan Crisps, Triscuit crackers, Chicken in a Biskit, sourdough
bread, French baguettes

Pickled:
green tomatoes, okra, peppers, olives, beets, jalapeno relish

Candy:
gummy bears, chocolate peanut butter cups, dark chocolates

Other:
mini pancakes topped with crème Fraiche and caviar (This is my son's
favorite. I took him to a private caviar tasting experience when he was nine
years old and there began his love affair with caviar.)

Chinese Barbecue Pork Hom Bao

Ingredients:

Dough:
1-16 ounce package Bột Bánh Bao (Steamed Dumpling Bun Flour)
*Follow the instructions on the package. You will need about 1/3 cup of
sugar and water or milk to prepare the dough according to the package.

Filling:
2-3 pounds pork shoulder, pork butt, or pork belly
¼ sweet yellow onion (diced)
2 cloves garlic (minced)
1 teaspoon salt
1 tablespoon olive oil or avocado oil

Marinade:
1 cup char siu sauce or char siu powder mix
2 tablespoon soy sauce
2 tablespoon oyster sauce
2 tablespoon honey
½ cup brown sugar
½ cup hoisin sauce
½ cup water
3 tablespoons cornstarch mixed with 2 tablespoons water

Other:
Steamer or a pot with a lid and flat-bottomed colander
Sheets of printer paper, cut into 10 circles, each about 3 inches wide
¼ cup flour for dusting the rolling pin and countertop
*If you do not have a rolling pin, use a highball drinking glass to roll the
dough.

Directions:
1. Follow the instructions on the banh bao flour package and separate
   the dough into 10 equal balls after the dough has risen.
2. While the dough rises, mix the first six ingredients of the marinade
   and taste. It should be sweet. Add more sugar or honey if you like a
   sweeter sauce.
3. Cut the pork into three sections and coat the pork in the marinade in
   a plastic bag for one hour.
4. Preheat the oven to 350 degrees.

5. Pour water into a roasting pan and put the pork onto a roasting rack. Place it in the pan, making sure the water level is below the pork.
6. Bake at 350 degrees F for 40 minutes.
7. In the meantime, spoon the residual marinade out of the bag and into a saucepan. Waste not, want not!
8. Add the last two ingredients in the marinade list (½ cup water and cornstarch/water mix) to the saucepan.
9. Bring the sauce to a boil then remove it from the heat and set it aside.
10. Once the pork in the oven is cooked, cut it into small bite-size cubes.
11. In a large saucepan, heat a tablespoon of oil and stir in the sweet yellow onion, garlic, and salt.
12. Add the marinade from the small saucepan to the large saucepan. Fold in the cubed pork and bring the sauce to a simmer until the meat is evenly coated and the sauce thickens to a jelly.
13. Set the pork aside to cool and continue thickening. You can put it in the freezer for 15 minutes to speed up the cooling.
14. Roll each dough ball into 4-inch circles. You can cover the dough with a cloth to keep it from drying out as you roll each ball.
15. Spoon the pork into the center of each circle and fold the dough up to the top. Pinch the peak with a twist to seal the hom bao.
16. Place the baos on a pre-cut sheet of paper and place the buns in the steamer or pot and flat-bottomed colander.
17. Steam for 10 minutes or until the dough is fluffy and cooked. Repeat until all the baos are cooked.
18. These freeze well. Wrap each bao in plastic wrap then aluminum foil and seal in a ziplock bag.
19. When you're feeling lazy to cook, take these out of the freezer, remove the aluminum foil, and microwave or steam them to eat. If you microwave them, drape a damp paper towel over the bao to lock in the moisture. A dry bao is an unhappy bao.

Gỏi Cuốn (Spring Rolls)

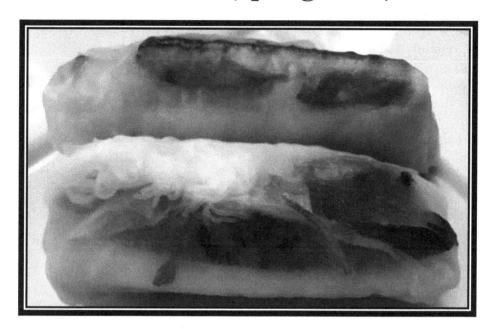

Spring rolls, like charcuterie boards, are versatile. What you roll in the rice paper is up to you! Here are our favorites. You cannot go wrong with any of the combinations from the list or make your own list.

Ingredients:

Meats:
pork butt or shoulder (marinated in your favorite seasonings, then grilled)
*You can also boil the pork for a fresh, healthy option
shrimp (peeled, deveined, then boiled or grilled, and halved lengthwise)
Chinese sausages (sliced into strips, then pan-fried)
pork belly (marinated in your favorite seasonings, then grilled)
cured ground pork a.k.a. nem nướng (See page 160 for a photo)
beef, chicken, or pork skewers (grilled)

Vegetables and herbs:
lettuce, cucumbers, pickled carrots and daikons, basil, bean sprouts, mint, perilla, coriander, watercress, cilantro

Wrapper:
rice paper (I prefer square ones but round ones are good too.)

Sauces:
sweet chili fish sauce (See page 137. This is a V-ADED staple.)
Indonesian peanut salad dressing
hoisin sauce (diluted with water so it isn't so thick)
Sriracha sauce, chili peppers, or your favorite hot sauce for spiciness

Other:
Optional: fried egg roll wrappers for an extra crunch to your roll (Take an egg roll wrapper, cut it into four squares, roll each square into a cylinder, and then deep fry them. Make as many fried wrapper rolls as you'd like for your spring rolls.)
vermicelli rice noodles (boil then drain the noodles as you would with pasta according to package instructions)

Directions:
1. Boil, bake, or grill your favorite meats (or use meats from leftover "Must-Go" meals) and slice them into strips.
2. Wash your favorite herbs and slice your cucumbers into 4-6 inch strips.
3. Prepare the vermicelli rice noodles and fried egg roll wrappers if you're using them for your spring rolls.
4. Prepare a large bowl of hot water. This is for dunking the rice paper to soften it.
5. Dip a sheet of rice paper into the bowl of hot water and shake off the excess water. You do not want your rice paper soggy.
6. Place the wet rice paper onto a plate and add your veggies and meats, vermicelli noodles, and crunchy fried egg roll wrappers.
7. Once the rice paper is soft, roll your spring roll like a burrito and tuck in the sides.
8. Dip it into your favorite sauce. Enjoy!

Mango Couscous Salad

Ingredients:

1 cup large pearl couscous
2 tablespoons olive oil
2 garlic cloves (minced)
1 cup red onions (chopped)
Optional:1 bell pepper (chopped, seeds and ribs removed)
½ teaspoon salt
2 tablespoons lime juice
Optional: ½ cup raisins
Optional: 1 tomato (chopped)
½ cup basil, cilantro, or parsley (chopped)
Optional: vegetable broth
2 mangos (peeled, pitted, and cubed)
* I prefer champagne or honey mangos - they are sweet and not stringy

Directions:
1. Prepare the couscous according to the package directions. For a more flavorful couscous substitute the water with vegetable broth.
2. Heat the oil in a large pan and saute the garlic, onions, and bell peppers.
3. Sprinkle in the salt and lime juice.
4. Toss in the raisins, tomato, and cilantro, parsley, or basil.
5. Turn off the heat and fold in the mangos. Drain excess liquids.
6. Serve immediately.
7. So simple to make, you should have your child or partner do it so you can relax, drink your wine, or read a book.

Patê Sô (Vietnamese Meat Pies)

Ingredients:

Filling:
1.5 pounds lean ground pork
1 cup dried wood ear mushrooms
1 small onion (peeled and chopped)
2 tablespoons fish sauce
2 tablespoons garlic powder
2 tablespoons ground white pepper
1 teaspoon salt
Optional: sugar

Dough:
4 packages puff pastry (NOT phyllo dough. I repeat. Not phyllo dough.)
2-4 tablespoons oil (Olive, Avocado, Vegetable, or Coconut)
½ cup flour
2 eggs (lightly beaten)

Other:
baking sheet

Directions:
1. Defrost puff pastries for thirty minutes until the dough is soft.
2. Preheat oven to 400 degrees F.
3. In a medium-sized bowl filled halfway with water, microwave the water for two minutes or heat the water in a small pot on a stove.
4. Soak mushrooms in the hot water until soft, about 10 minutes.
5. Drain the water, rinse the mushrooms in cold water, and then chop the mushrooms into small pieces.
6. In a large mixing bowl, combine pork, mushrooms, onion, fish sauce, garlic powder, white pepper, and salt. Mix well.
7. Yippee, you get to do a taste test. Sauté a tablespoon of the filling in a frying pan and sample the flavor. If it is too salty, add a little sugar to the meat filling.
8. Roll the sheets of pastry puff dough onto a floured surface and cut the dough into 2-inch circles using a biscuit cutter or drinking glass.
9. Brush half of the dough circles with the lightly beaten egg wash. The other half of the dough circles will be the tops of the meat pies. The egg wash will make the pastry puff golden and extra flaky once baked.

10. Roll the filling into 1-inch balls and place each ball into the bottom halves of the dough circles.
11. Cover each meat pie with the other half of the dough circles.
12. Use a fork to seal the edges of the meat pies.
13. Brush the egg wash on the tops of each egg pie and put them onto a lightly oiled baking sheet. (I put parchment paper onto the baking sheet and coat it with oil.)
14. Bake at 400 degrees F for 20-25 minutes.
15. Enjoy the pies right away while they are warm and crispy. I like to toast the meat pies the next morning for breakfast with my coffee and pack them in my son and husband's lunch bag.

The perfect tailgate/stadium snack or lunch on the go!

Pork and Shrimp Wontons

Ingredients:

Filling:
1 package (14 ounces) cured ground pork for meatballs a.k.a. *nem nướng* and can be found in the frozen section of Asian markets. (You can make your own *nem nướng* if you're inclined. I go straight to the freezer section because I'm not getting any younger. Yep, the wrinkles are sagging as we speak.)
2 pounds shrimp (peeled, deveined, ground in a food processor)
1 cup dried wood ear mushrooms(soaked in hot water for 15 minutes until soft, then drained and chopped)
2 inches ginger (peeled and minced)
1 cup green onions (chopped)
2 tablespoons soy sauce
1 teaspoon of rice wine vinegar
2 teaspoons sesame oil
2 tablespoons cornstarch

Wrappers:
2 packages (16 ounces each) wonton wrappers (separated)
*Each package has around 85 wonton sheets. I prefer the yellow ones. This is a good job for the adult-in-training in your household. Little child fingers are good at separating wrappers, but make sure those fingers are clean.

Other:

Optional: Peanut oil for deep frying the wontons (If you are steaming the wontons, no oil is needed.)

Optional: Steamer or pot with a lid and flat-bottomed colander

Directions:
1. Combine all the filling ingredients in a large bowl and mix well with a wooden spoon or your hands. (Are your fingernails trimmed?)
2. Put a cup of hot water into a mug. Don't drink it! The water is to seal the edges of the wonton wrappers.
3. Spoon a tablespoon of the filling into a wonton wrapper.
4. Using your finger or a silicone brush, wet the edges of the wonton wrapper with water to moisten edges.
5. Gather the edges together and press the sides together to seal the wontons. You can fold them like gyozas or be fancy and make stars.
6. Wontons can be steamed or deep-fried for 10 minutes and enjoyed in a noodle soup, as an appetizer, or as an accompaniment to rice and noodle bowls.
7. I freeze extra wontons to fry or steam later on those lazy days.
8. If you bite the wontons and notice the meat is pink, don't worry. The cured ground pork (*nem mướng*) has a tint of red due to the food coloring. But what are you biting it in half for? Pop the whole thing in your mouth already!

Salad Niçoise (French Summer Salad)

The French summer salad is traditionally made with tomatoes, hardboiled eggs, olives, and tuna. Feel free to add artichokes, capers, blanched green beans, radishes, potatoes, cucumbers, red onions, pickled okra, pinto beans, carrots, bell peppers, arugula or lettuce, and anything else you like.

Dressing:
¼ cup lemon juice or white wine vinegar
1 clove garlic (minced)
1 teaspoon Dijon mustard
¼ teaspoon of sea salt
¼ teaspoon ground black pepper
½ teaspoon honey
¼ cup olive oil
½ teaspoon fresh basil

Whisk together the dressing ingredients. Drizzle the vinaigrette over your perfect Niçoise.

MAIN COURSES

"I'm amazed by your culinary talent as much as by your writing. Your food posts are as intimate as your stories in your book."
—**Hirut Negash, Instagrammer**

Bánh Mì Sandwich (Vietnamese Baguette)

Ingredients:

French bread or baguette (toasted)
cucumber (sliced into thin strips)
cilantro (leaves and stem)
pâté
grilled pork or roasted chicken (I like the store-bought rotisserie chicken)
*See page 148 for a barbecue pork marinade from the Chinese Barbecue Pork Hom Bao recipe
soy sauce
optional: jalapenos or chili peppers, fresh or pickled (sliced thinly)
optional: hot sauce (e.g. Sriracha)
mayonnaise (regular or Vietnamese-style)
pickled carrots (shredded)
pickled daikons (shredded)

Vietnamese mayonnaise:
2 egg yolks
¾ cup vegetable oil
Pinch of salt

Directions for the mayonnaise:
1. Using a hand mixer, beat two egg yolks for one minute on medium-high speed.
2. Add one spoon of oil and continue beating for 30 seconds. Repeat this step until the oil is gone. You do not want the oil and eggs to separate.
3. Add a pinch of salt and mix in. This will yield a cup of fluffy, creamy mayonnaise, like whipped butter. Store in the fridge for up to 3 days.

Pickled carrots and daikons:
1 carrot, thinly sliced (peel and discard the skin)
1 daikon, thinly sliced (peel and discard the skin)
Vinegar
Sugar
Salt

Directions for pickling the carrots and daikons:
1. In a glass jar, put in the shredded carrots and daikon.
2. Fill the jar with distilled white vinegar.
3. Add equal amounts of salt and sugar, one teaspoon each at a time.
4. Stir and taste. Add more salt and sugar as needed until you get a tangy, sweet taste.
5. Seal the jar and refrigerate for a minimum of one hour before eating.

Assembling the sandwich:
1. Toast the baguette and slice it in half lengthwise.
2. Spread the mayonnaise on the top and bottom of the baguette. Don't be skimping on the mayonnaise now. Be generous.
3. Spread a thick layer of pâté on the bottom and work it into the bread like you're massaging the sandwich.
4. Drizzle some soy sauce on the top part of the sandwich. You have to give the top slice some love too. Balance is good.
5. Add slices of pork or chicken. If you're a glutton like me, you already added both. Yes, I see you.
6. Now comes the healthy stuff: cucumber slices, pickled carrots, and daikons. Don't forget the cilantro. Herbs need love too.
7. Finally, add some heat and do your hot chili/hot sauce dance.
8. Taste the nirvana in your mouth and say, "Hallelujah!"

Bánh Mì Bò Kho
(Braised Beef Stew with French Baguette)

Ingredients:

4 New York Steaks (cut into cubes)
French baguettes
2 tablespoons olive oil
4 cloves garlic (minced)
1 scallion (sliced)
2 carrots (peeled and cut 1-inch pieces)
1 large potato (peeled and cut into 1-inch pieces)
1 large sweet potato (peeled and cut into 1-inch pieces)

Marinade:
2 tablespoons soy sauce
2 tablespoons hoisin sauce
1 teaspoons salt
2 tablespoons Vietnamese Beef Stew Seasoning (Bột Bò Kho)

Broth:
32 ounces chicken broth (yes, chicken, even though this is beef stew)
1 12-fluid ounce can coconut soda
2 tablespoons tomato paste
1 tablespoon sweet soy sauce
1 medium yellow onion (peeled, cut in half)
2 inches ginger (peeled, minced)
2 stalks lemongrass (cut in half & tied together with string)
3 star anise
3 dried bay leaves

Garnishes (optional):
basil
cilantro (chopped)
red onions or scallions (sliced thin)
chili peppers (sliced)

Directions:
1. Crack open a bottle of beer or pop the cork. You're going to want to leisurely enjoy a beverage while making this.
2. Bring a pot of water to a boil and add the cubed New York Steaks. Boil for two minutes then drain and rinse the beef to remove the impurities. Don't be lazy and skip this step.

3. In a large bowl, whisk together soy sauce, hoisin sauce, salt, and beef stew seasoning. Taste and add more soy sauce or hoisin sauce according to your taste.
4. Toss in the cubed beef and marinate for thirty minutes.
5. In a large frying pan, heat the oil on medium-high heat. Add garlic and scallions. Stir-fry for ten seconds.
6. Add the marinated beef and its sauce. Reduce heat to medium.
7. Stir-fry the meat for 3-5 minutes. Meat should be evenly coated with the marinade and cooked to medium-well or well done.
8. Add chicken broth, coconut soda, tomato paste, sweet soy sauce, yellow onion, ginger, lemongrass, star anise, and bay leaves.
9. Increase temperature to medium-high and bring the broth to a boil. Once it begins to boil, cover the pot with a lid, and reduce the heat to low.
10. Simmer the broth for twenty minutes.
11. Add potatoes and carrots. Simmer, covered, for another 20 minutes.
12. Check the tenderness of the meat and vegetables. Simmer for another twenty minutes if you prefer more tenderness. Otherwise, turn off the stove.
13. Toast the French baguettes and serve on the side.
14. Spoon the stew into a bowl and garnish with cilantro, basil, and red onions or scallions.

"Can't get enough of Snow's Kitchen."
—**Manuel Gonzales, Senior District Sales Manager, RBDC**

Bánh Xèo (Vietnamese Sizzling Crepes)

Ingredients:

¼ cup vegetable oil
sweet chili fish sauce (See page 137)

Batter:
2 green onions (thinly sliced)
1 package of bột bánh xèo flour mix (crepe flour mix)
*The flour mix will call for water but I do half and half of a carbonated soda (e.g. club soda or coconut soda) and a light beer (e.g. Bud Light).

*You can make your own batter by whisking together:
1 cup rice flour
1 tablespoon cornstarch
1 teaspoon turmeric powder
2 cups club soda or coconut soda
1 cup light beer
1/2 cup coconut milk
1 teaspoon salt

Filling:
1 pound boneless country-style pork shoulder or pork belly (thinly sliced)
1 pound medium-size shrimp (peeled, deveined)
1 small onion or scallion (peeled, halved, and thinly sliced)
2 cups bean sprouts

Sides:
mustard leaves, red-leaf lettuce, or romaine lettuce
1 cucumber (cut into 3-4 inch spears)
cilantro, mint, perilla, fish wort, and/or basil
chili peppers or hot sauce
rice paper (if you prefer to make it a crepe spring roll)

Other:
very good non-stick frying pan or cast-iron pan.
silicone brush

Directions:

1. Prepare the batter according to the instructions on the bánh xèo flour mix or make your batter from scratch if you're not lazy like me.
2. Add chopped green onions to the batter and refrigerate the batter uncovered for a minimum of 30 minutes.
3. Heat a good cast-iron pan or non-stick frying pan on medium-high heat. If your pan is not good, add a little oil to the pan.
4. Once the pan is hot, add one-fourth of the sliced pork. Reduce heat to medium-low and stir-fry the meat for three minutes.
5. Transfer the pork into a bowl and repeat stir-frying the rest of the meat in batches. Do not let the pan burn. Stir constantly.
6. Do not crowd the pan. You want each slice of meat to be crisp. Transfer all the cooked meat to a bowl.
7. Add the shrimp to the pan and stir-fry for another few minutes until cooked. Transfer the shrimp to a separate bowl.
8. Remove the batter from the refrigerator and whisk the batter until it is evenly mixed.
9. Turn the heat up to medium. Once the pan is hot, add a few pieces of onion slices (or scallions), a couple of pork pieces, a couple of shrimps, and a sprinkle of bean sprouts.
10. Ladle some batter into the frying pan and cover the pan evenly and thinly with the batter. (The thinner the better so that it is crispy.)
11. Cover the pan and let it sizzle for 2-3 minutes.
12. Once the edges start to lift and turn light brown, remove the lid.
13. Using a small silicone brush, brush the edges with vegetable oil and let some of the oil seep under the crepe batter.
14. Lower the heat a touch if you need to and pan-fry uncovered for another three minutes.
15. Fold the crepe in half with a spatula and transfer the crepe to a plate. It is best to eat one straight from the pan while the crepe is crunchy.
16. Repeat with the rest of the batter and filling until you run out. Make sure you stir and mix your batter each time as the flour settles to the bottom.
17. Serve the crepes with vegetables and herbs of your choice. Drizzle sweet chili fish sauce on top. (See page 137.)
18. If you prefer, you may roll your crepe in softened rice paper or lettuce and dip the roll into the sweet chili fish sauce like a spring roll.

Bò Bougie Ngon (Beouf Bourgignon)

Ingredients:

2 tablespoons olive oil or ghee
1 package bacon (cut into 2-inch strips)
3 pounds of beef brisket, sirloin, New York steak, or chuck roast (cut into 2-inch cubes)
2 carrots (peeled, cut into bite-size pieces)
2 sweet yellow onions (minced) or 2 bags of pearl onions (remove skin)
*You can use a combination of both sweet yellow onions and pearl onions
2 tablespoons garlic (minced)
1 tablespoon salt
1 teaspoon ground black pepper
3 tablespoons flour
1 pound of mushrooms (sliced)
1 tablespoon butter

Broth:
2 bottles of red wine – although you'll only use 3 cups of it for the broth. The rest is to keep you company while you cook and eat. Burgundy wines are best. I prefer pinot noir and merlot wine in the $15-20 range. Do not use cheap wines for this exquisite stew otherwise, it will not be "bougie ngon."
32 ounces of beef broth
6 ounce can tomato paste
2 tablespoons beef bouillon (I prefer Better Than Bouillon Premium Roasted Beef Base)
2 bay leaves

Garnish:
¼ cup fresh parsley (chopped)

Sides:
starchy foods like noodles, rice, mashed potatoes, baguettes, or polenta

Other:
large pot or dutch oven
slotted spatula or spoon

Directions:

1. Heat the oil or ghee in the pot or dutch oven over medium-high heat and saute the bacon until crisp. Remove the bacon with a slotted spoon.
2. Sear the beef in the bacon grease for one minute on each side. Do this in batches. Do not crowd the pan. Remove the beef and set it aside with the bacon.
3. Saute the carrots, onions, and garlic in the same pot for 3 minutes. Add the beef and bacon back to the pot or dutch oven.
4. Sprinkle salt, black pepper, and flour onto the beef and stir fry.
5. Add 3 cups of wine, the beef broth, the tomato paste, and beef bouillon base to the pot.
6. Stir until the tomato paste is mixed evenly into the broth.
7. Add the bay leaves.
8. Bring to a boil and let it boil for 3-5 minutes.
9. Reduce heat to low, cover the pot, and let it simmer for two hours. This is when you enjoy the extra wine you purchased. Check the sauce after one hour. It should start to thicken. Sample the broth.
10. At the two hour mark, taste the broth and sample the beef. It should be tender and bursting with flavor.
11. In a pan, heat the butter and stir-fry the mushrooms for five minutes.
12. Add the mushrooms to the dutch oven. Cover with the lid. Turn off the heat and let it sit for five minutes.
13. Garnish with parsley and serve with your favorite starchy food.

Bò Lúc Lắc (Shaken Beef)

Ingredients:

1.5 pounds beef brisket or sirloin (cut into 1-inch cubes)
1 red onion (peeled, thinly sliced)
2 bunches of watercress or arugula
2 tomatoes (thinly sliced)
2 tablespoons cooking oil

Marinade:
4 cloves garlic (minced)
1.5 tablespoons sugar
2 tablespoons oyster sauce
1 tablespoon fish sauce
1 tablespoon sesame oil
1 teaspoon thick sweet soy sauce

Vinaigrette dressing:
½ cup rice vinegar
1.5 tablespoons sugar
½ tablespoon salt

Directions:
1. Prepare the marinade by mixing the six ingredients in a medium-size bowl.
2. Stir in the beef and coat the meat evenly in the marinade. Let it sit for a minimum of 30 minutes but ideally an hour.
3. Meanwhile, mix the vinaigrette dressing ingredients and taste. It should be a balance of sweet, salty, and tangy.
4. Pour half of the vinaigrette over the thinly sliced onions and let it sit for 30 minutes in the fridge, covered in plastic wrap, to pickle.
5. Prepare a bed of watercress or arugula on a serving plate and put slices of tomatoes on top. Cover and refrigerate until you are ready to serve the dish.
6. Heat a frying pan over medium-high heat with cooking oil. Once the oil is hot, add the beef in batches to the frying pan. Sear the beef for two minutes.
7. After two minutes, shake your bootie and the frying pan at the same time to sear the other sides of the beef for another two minutes.
8. If you do not shake your bootie, you're doing it wrong and your shaken beef will not turn out delicious. That is the secret.

9. Repeat steps 6 and 7 until all the beef is cooked to your desired doneness. I prefer medium-rare.
10. Spoon the beef onto the bed of tomatoes and watercress or arugula. You can toss the extra juice in the pan or drizzle it on top of the beef and salad. I drizzle the juice and a few tablespoons of the vinaigrette dressing on top of the beef!
11. Add the pickled onions on top and enjoy your shaken beef. I smother my salad in the vinaigrette dressing!

Bún Riêu Cua (Crab Vermicelli Soup)

Ingredients:

1 package rice vermicelli noodles
2 pounds pork spare ribs
1 - 3 ounce package dried shrimp
2 tsp salt
1 large lump rock sugar
¼ cup fish sauce
1 small whole onion (peeled, quartered)
12 jumbo prawns (peeled, deveined)
1 pound ground pork
4 cloves garlic
2 tablespoon mushroom seasoning powder
1 teaspoon ground black pepper
1 - 5.6 oz can minced prawn in spices (gia vị nấu bún riêu)
1 - 14 oz can minced crab in spices (riêu cua)
1+ lb crab meat
3 eggs beaten
1 - 20 ounce container fried tofu (cut in half)
6 large Roma tomatoes (quartered)

Herbs and Garnishes:
*Optional – pick and choose your favorite herbs
cilantro (chopped)
green onions (chopped)
perilla leaves (remove stems)
watercress (chopped into 1-inch pieces)
bean sprouts (rinsed)
lime (sliced into six wedges)

Other:
food processor

Directions:
1. Bring a large pot of water to a boil on high heat.
2. Add the pork spare ribs to the pot and bring to boil for 5 minutes.
3. Drain and rinse the pork.
4. Start a fresh pot of water, filled ¾ full, and add the pork back in along with dried shrimp.
5. Bring the water back to a boil, then lower the heat to medium to simmer.

6. Add salt, rock sugar, and fish sauce to the pot.
7. In a food processor, chop together the onion, prawns, and garlic.
8. In a large bowl, combine the ground pork with the prawns.
9. Sprinkle in the mushroom seasoning powder and black pepper to the bowl.
10. Add the entire can of minced prawn in spices, can of minced crab in spices, crab meat, and beaten eggs into the bowl.
11. Mix well, then spoon the pork, shrimp, and crab mixture into the pot of simmering water, pork ribs, and dried shrimp.
12. Let the broth simmer for twenty minutes without the lid.
13. Meanwhile, bring a fresh pot of water to a boil and cook the vermicelli noodles. Once it is cooked, drain the noodles and rinse.
14. Add the fried tofu and tomatoes into the simmering broth and let it simmer for another ten minutes.
15. Taste the broth. Add more salt if needed or a touch of sugar or another rock sugar if it is too salty. If the broth is a little on the salty side, it's okay, as it will balance out once you eat it with vermicelli noodles and lime.
16. To serve, put noodles into a bowl. Spoon the crab soup into the bowl. Garnish with your favorite herbs.
17. Squeeze a lime wedge into the broth and enjoy.

Cá Kho Tộ (Caramelized Braised Catfish)

Ingredients:

2 pounds catfish filets (bone-in, skin on)
3 tablespoons salt to clean the fish
3 tablespoons oil
6 cloves garlic (minced)
1 small onion (minced)
1 bunch green onions (chopped)
2 teaspoons salt
2 teaspoons ground black pepper
1 tablespoon thick caramelized soy sauce
3 tablespoons fish sauce
1 can coconut soda

Optional:
chili peppers (sliced) or flakes
large clay pot
*I use a large saucepan to braise the catfish, then transfer it to a clay pot once the fish and sauce reduces down and is cooked. It is traditional to cook and serve the braised catfish in a clay pot.

Sides:
cooked jasmine rice

Other:
Optional: clay pot, otherwise, a large saucepan works great

Directions:
1. Sprinkle 3 tablespoons of salt on the catfish filets and rub the salt all over the fish. Rinse in warm water and pat dry with a paper towel.
2. Marinate the catfish in salt, black pepper, fish sauce, and thick caramelized soy sauce for five minutes.
3. In a large saucepan, heat the oil on medium-high heat.
4. Open the windows and turn on the fan. It will smell pungent but I promise the braised catfish will be so delicious.
5. Stir-fry the garlic and onions for 2 minutes. Reduce the heat to medium.
6. Add the catfish filets to the saucepan. Do not crowd the pan.
7. Pour in the coconut soda and cover with a lid. Simmer for ten minutes.

8. If anyone asks what the smell is, blame it on them, your pet, child, or spouse.
9. Gently flip the catfish filets over and simmer another ten minutes with the lid on, over medium heat.
10. Taste the sauce. It should be a balance of sweet and salty. Add salt or sugar as needed.
11. Remove the lid and continue simmering. Spoon the sauce over the fish repeatedly for ten minutes.
12. Garnish with green onions. If you like it spicy, add chili peppers or chili flakes.
13. Turn off the heat, put the lid on, and let it continue to cook for another 5-10 minutes.
14. Optional – transfer the catfish and sauce to a clay pot.
15. Serve the catfish with a bed of jasmine rice.

"Food is AMAZING, packed full of flavor, and definitely made from love."
—Frances Moore, Foodie

Cà Ri Gà (Yellow Curry Chicken)

Ingredients:

Marinade:
1 pound chicken breast tenders (cut into 1-inch pieces)
1 pound boneless chicken thighs (fat trimmed, cut into 1-inch pieces)
1 tablespoons salt
1 tablespoon sugar
1 teaspoon ground black pepper
2 tablespoons granulated chicken flavor soup base mix (or chicken bouillon)
2 tablespoons yellow curry powder or curry base
2 stalks lemongrass (mince 2 tablespoons of it and set aside for the marinade)

*You'll need **two stalks of lemongrass** total. Two tablespoons of minced lemongrass will go into the marinade and the remainder will go into the curry broth

Curry broth:
2 tablespoons olive oil
2 inches ginger (peeled and minced)
2 cloves garlic (peeled and minced)
1 small scallion or sweet onion (chopped)
32-ounce chicken broth
2-14.5 fluid ounce cans coconut cream/coconut milk
2 stalks lemongrass (with the remainder of the lemongrass, cut both stalks in half and smash the ends with a mortar and pestle to release the aroma and flavors. Tie the stalks together.)
2 tablespoons sugar
1 large sweet potato (peeled and cubed)
2 carrots (peeled and cubed)
2 large russet potatoes (peeled and cubed)

Optional garnish:
cilantro (chopped)

Sides:
French baguettes (toasted)
cooked jasmine rice (cooked)
rice noodles (cooked, drained)

Directions:

1. Mix the first eight ingredients and marinate for thirty minutes in the refrigerator.
2. In a wok or pot, heat olive oil on medium-high heat.
3. Add ginger, garlic, and scallions. Stir fry for two minutes.
4. Add marinated chicken. Lower heat to medium. Stir fry the chicken until it is cooked, about five minutes.
5. Add chicken broth, coconut cream, sugar, and stalks of lemongrass.
6. Increase heat to medium-high and cook for 10 minutes uncovered, stirring often.
7. Add sweet potatoes, carrots, and russet potatoes. Stir.
8. Lower the heat to medium.
9. Cover the pot with a lid and let it simmer for 20 minutes.
10. Taste the curry and add more salt or sugar according to taste.
11. Once the vegetables and chicken are tender, serve the curry in a bowl and garnish with cilantro.
12. Ladle a serving into a secret-stash container and hide this from everyone. The curry will go fast and when everyone is sad it is gone, you'll have your secret stash for the final meal! Worth the secret!
13. Serve with rice, rice noodles, or a toasted baguette.
    (I prefer dipping my warm, toasted baguette in the curry.)

"Amy's sweet potato and chicken curry is like a warm hug on a cold rainy day! My favorite!"
—Leah Dimino, Real Estate Agent

Cháo Hải Sản (Seafood Congee)

Congee is also called rice porridge and is often cooked with chicken. The seafood congee is not as commonly known, but it is great comfort street food. I like mine with clams and shrimp.

Ingredients:

2-32 ounce box chicken broth
2 cups water
2 cups jasmine rice (washed and drained a few times until the water is clear)
2 tablespoons olive oil
2 tablespoons scallions (peeled and minced)
2 cloves garlic (minced)
2 tablespoons ginger (peeled and minced)
1 pound large shrimp (peeled, deveined)
2-3 cups clam meat (cooked, no shell)*
¼ cup green onions (chopped)
¼ cup cilantro (chopped)
salt and black pepper to taste
2 tablespoons fried onions (optional)
2 tablespoons fried garlic (optional)

*If you can find clam meat without shells in the frozen section of most grocery stores, that is best. Otherwise, steam your clams until they are cooked. It is optional to leave the clams in the shells.

Directions:

1. Pour all the chicken broth and 2 cups water into a large pot and bring to a boil on medium-high heat.
2. Meanwhile, wash the jasmine rice to remove excess starch and drain. Repeat until the water runs clear.
3. Once the broth comes to a boil, add the jasmine rice to the pot and stir constantly so it does not stick.
4. Reduce heat to low, cover the pot with a lid, and let the rice simmer. Stir every ten minutes to make sure the rice is not burning or clumping together.
5. Heat the olive oil in a frying pan on medium heat.
6. Add the scallions, garlic, and ginger, and stir fry for two minutes to release the fragrance.
7. Add the shrimp and sauté for 3-5 minutes until the shrimp is no longer translucent.

8. Add the clams and stir-fry the ensemble for three minutes.
9. Turn off the stove and set the shrimp and clams aside.
10. Stir the rice every ten minutes to make sure the rice is not clumping or burning at the bottom.
11. Continue simmering with the lid on for an hour, checking every ten minutes.
12. After an hour, your congee is done. The rice should be broken and mushy like porridge. Add more water if you prefer your congee more brothy than thick.
13. Turn off the heat and fold the shrimp and clam mixture into the pot of congee, including the juices, garlic, onions, and ginger.
14. Add salt and pepper to taste.
15. Garnish with cilantro and green onions.
16. Optional garnishes: Top with fried onions and/or fried garlic for a little crunch.

"I always look forward to your food. Hands down the best! Hmmm!"
—Jeff Cole, Operations Manager, Red Bull Distribution Company

Chili

Ingredients:

Vegetables:
1 red bell pepper (minced)
1 orange bell pepper (minced)
2 stalks celery (minced)
1 onion (minced)
1 jalapeno pepper (minced with seeds)
3 cloves garlic (minced)

Canned/Bottled Ingredients:
2 tablespoons hot sauce
2 cans ranch style chili beans with the liquid
1 can red kidney beans (drained)
2 cans diced tomatoes with the liquid
1 small 6-ounce can tomato paste

Meats:
1 pound bacon (fried, save the bacon grease)
2-3 pounds lean ground beef
5 Italian sausages (cut into ½ inch pieces)

Seasonings:
3 tablespoons chili powder
1 tablespoon dried oregano
1 teaspoon cumin
1 teaspoon parsley (fresh or dried)
1 teaspoon basil (fresh or dried)
1 teaspoon garlic salt
1teaspoon black pepper
1 teaspoon cayenne pepper
1 teaspoon paprika
1 teaspoon red chili flakes
1 tablespoon sugar
1 tablespoon Worcestershire sauce (worsty-shir-shir thing)
2 tablespoons beef bouillon powder or concentrate

Garnishes/Toppings:
cilantro (chopped)
sour cream
cheddar cheese (shredded)

avocado (cubed)
cheddar cheese-flavored Fritos
bacon (crumbled)

Side:
Jiffy Corn Bread Muffin Mix or your favorite cornbread recipe

Directions:
1. Toss the first six vegetable ingredients into a food processor and chop on low until minced evenly. Dump it all into a large slow cooker, crockpot, or dutch oven.
2. Add the next five ingredients into the slow cooker, i.e., your favorite hot sauce, chili beans with liquids, kidney beans (drained), diced tomatoes with liquids, and tomato paste.
3. On medium-high heat, in a large frying pan, fry up all the bacon and set aside. Use paper towels to soak up the excess fat of the cooked bacon.
4. Reduce heat to medium, keeping the bacon grease in the pan.
5. Add the ground beef and Italian sausages to the pan. Use a blunt wooden spoon to break up the meat until it is cooked thoroughly and in small bits.
6. Use a slotted ladle or spoon and transfer the ground up meats into the slow cooker. Discard the excess fat and liquid in the pan.
7. Divide the cooked bacon in half and crumble the bacon into small pieces. Half will go into the slow cooker, half will be used as a garnish.
8. Add all the seasonings into the slow cooker, crockpot, or dutch oven.
9. Stir and mix the ingredients evenly. Cook on high for five hours in the slow cooker or simmer on low on the stove, with the lid on, for five hours. Check every hour if you are cooking the chili on the stovetop. Stir frequently to make sure the chili is not burnt or clumping at the bottom.
10. Serve the chili with your choice of toppings: cilantro, cheddar cheese, sour cream, avocado, bacon crumbles, and/or cheddar cheese-flavored Fritos.
11. Be prepared to enjoy this crack chili because it tastes better the next day!

Cơm Chiên (Fried Rice)

Ingredients:

2 cups uncooked jasmine rice
4 tablespoons bacon grease or vegetable oil
3 Chinese sausages (diced)
3 large eggs (lightly beaten)
3 cloves garlic (minced)
1 pound large shrimp (peeled, deveined)
½ cup carrots (peeled, diced)
2 tablespoons soy sauce seasoning (I use Maggi brand)
salt and pepper to taste

Other:
rice cooker
wok or large saucepan
colander
slotted spoon
wooden spoon or spatula

Directions:
1. Wash the rice in water and drain the water. Repeat until the water runs clear.
2. Put the jasmine rice into a rice cooker pot. Cook the rice **al dente**. Add fresh water to the pot and use your middle finger to measure the water level. With the tip of your finger resting on top of the rice, the water level should be below the first joint of your finger (about ¾ of your finger is submerged in water). **Note**: To make the perfect rice, fill the water to the first joint line of your finger, but for fried rice, cook al dente.
3. Once the rice is done, unplug the rice cooker and let it cool.
4. Once the rice is cool, use a spoon to stir up the rice. It should be on the dry side. Store the rice in the refrigerator for 4+ hours.
5. Spoon a tablespoon of oil or bacon grease (preferred) into a frying pan and heat the grease on medium-high heat.
6. Once the grease is hot, add the diced Chinese sausages and stir-fry for a few minutes until the sausage is cooked – about five minutes.
7. Using a slotted spoon, scoop out the cooked Chinese sausages into a large bowl. Reserve any excess grease in the frying pan.
8. Add another spoon of grease or oil to the pan and add the lightly beaten eggs. Hard-scramble the eggs with a wooden spoon or spatula.

9. Remove the eggs and add them to the same bowl as the Chinese sausages. Reserve any excess grease in the frying pan.
10. Spoon a tablespoon of the bacon grease or vegetable oil into the same frying pan and add the minced garlic cloves and shrimp. Sauté until the shrimp is almost cooked.
11. Add the diced carrots and continue sautéing until the shrimp is cooked and the carrots are soft.
12. Remove the carrots and shrimp and add them to the bowl with the sausages and eggs.
13. Add the last tablespoon of bacon grease or oil into the pan and add the cold rice by breaking it up with your hands. There should be no clumps. Crumble and separate the rice kernels.
14. Add soy sauce and continue stir-frying until the rice is evenly coated and uniform in color. Add more soy sauce if needed.
15. Sprinkle salt and pepper to the fried rice. Mix and taste. Add more according to your taste.
16. Drain any excess juices from your bowl of Chinese sausages, eggs, carrots, and shrimp through a colander so that it is dry.
17. Dump the bowl of sausages, eggs, carrots, and shrimp into the pan/wok.
18. Stir-fry and mix evenly, then turn off the heat. Let the rice cool down a little before serving.

Mì Sài Gòn (Saigonese Egg Noodle Soup)

Ingredients:

Chinese Barbecue Pork:
½ cup Chinese barbecue char siu seasoning mix
½ cup water
½ cup soy sauce
2 pounds pork loin

Broth:
2 pounds pork bones
½ package of dried squid
1-3 ounce package dried shrimp
1 sweet yellow onion
7 ounces sweet radish (about 4 pieces)
salt and sugar to taste

Other:
20 large prawns (peeled, deveined)
sesame oil
yellow egg noodles
baby bok choy (washed thoroughly)

Garnishes:
green onions (chopped)
basil
sawtooth herb (chopped)

Optional:
steamed pork and shrimp wontons (See page 159.)

Directions:
1. Preheat the oven to 370 degrees.
2. In a large bowl, whisk together the Chinese barbecue Char Siu seasoning mix, water, and soy sauce.
3. Add the pork loins to the mixture and marinate for 30 minutes.
4. Place the marinated pork loins on a non-stick baking sheet, roasting pan, or rectangular glass baking pan.
5. Pour the excess barbecue sauce on top of the pork.
6. Bake for 30 minutes. Turn the pork over and bake another 15 minutes. Turn off the oven and leave the pork in the oven for fifteen minutes.

7. Slice the pork into strips and set aside on a platter.
8. In a large pot, add pork bones, dried squid, dried shrimp, yellow onion, and sweet radishes.
9. Fill the pot with water leaving two inches at the top.
10. Bring the pot to a boil and remove the scum with a ladle.
11. Reduce heat to low and let the broth simmer for an hour uncovered. Continue removing the scum as needed until the broth looks clear.
12. Add salt and sugar to desired taste. The broth should be semi-sweet.
13. Bring a small pot of water to a boil and cook the prawns in the water for five minutes. Turn off the heat and let the prawns continue to cook in the hot water for five minutes.
14. Drain the shrimp into a colander and add them to the platter with the pork.
15. Fill a large pot half full with water and bring it to a boil.
16. Add a tablespoon of sesame oil to the water and the egg noodles.
17. Cook the noodles for 2-4 minutes, stirring constantly. Do not allow the noodles to stick. You will want the noodles **al dente**.
18. Drain the noodles and rinse under cool water.
19. Drizzle 1-2 tablespoons of sesame oil onto the noodles and toss to coat evenly.
20. Turn off the stove and cover the broth with a lid. Let it sit for 15 minutes.
21. Strain the broth through a colander into another large pot. Save the pork bones. Once the bones are cool to the touch, pick off the meat and add them to the platter with the prawns and barbecue pork.
22. Discard the onion, dried shrimp, dried squid, and sweet radishes.
23. Return the broth to the stove and let it simmer with the lid on.
24. Wash the baby bok choy then steam them for 10-15 minutes until tender.
25. Add the bok choy to the vegetable platter alongside the chopped green onions, chopped sawtooth herbs, and basil leaves.
26. Prepare your egg noodle soup bowl with egg noodles, pork, shrimp, wontons (optional), bok choy, and garnishes.
27. Ladle hot broth into the bowl and enjoy!

Phở (Vietnamese Beef Noodle Soup)

Phở broth is traditionally slow-simmered in a pot for hours but thanks to the instant pot, the same delicious broth can be done in less than three hours.

Broth:
½ pound beef bones with marrow
3 pounds oxtail (cut into 1 inch thick pieces)
2 inches ginger (peeled)
1 medium sweet yellow onion (peeled)
1 tablespoon salt
1 package pho seasoning (I use Pho Hoa Pasteur. It comes in a red 2 oz. box. Inside there are two packets. You will need only one.)
¾ cup fish sauce (I use Viet Huong fish sauce. It comes in a 24 fl. oz. bottle with a pink label and a picture of three crabs.)

Meats (all optional to your preference):
1 pound ribeye beef (thinly sliced)
1 pound eye of round beef (thinly sliced)
oxtail from above in the broth section
tripe (cooked strips)
Vietnamese beef meatballs (bò viên)

Herbs and Garnishes (all optional to your preference):
soybean sprouts
peppermint or spearmint leaves
Thai basil leaves
fish wort
perilla leaves
cilantro
chili peppers
limes (cut into 6-8 wedges)

Condiments (all optional):
hoisin sauce (I use Lee Kum Kee hoisin sauce with a purple label.)
fresh chili peppers (sliced) or hot chili sauce (I use Sriracha.)

Noodles:
14 oz, package rice (pho) stick noodles (3 mm wide)

Other:
large 8 qt. Instant Pot
colander

Directions:

1. Fill a large pot half full with water and bring to a boil on high heat.
2. Add beef bones and oxtails to the pot.
3. Boil for five minutes to remove the impurities.
4. Drain into a large colander and wash the bones and oxtail in cold water.
5. In a large Instant Pot (or large pot if you do not have an Instant Pot) add the beef bones, oxtail, ginger, onion, salt, a package of pho seasoning (Pho Hoa Pasteur), fish sauce, and 16 cups of water.
   **I have an Instant Pot Ultra 8 quart multicooker.
   Set the Instant Pot to Pressure Cook on high for one hour.
   **It will take 30+ minutes for the Instant Pot to reach pressure cook temperature, plus one hour of pressure cooking.
   If you are cooking the broth the traditional method, in a pot on the stove, bring the broth to a boil on medium-high heat. Then reduce the heat to low and let simmer, covered, for 4-6 hours, until the oxtail meat is tender and falls off the bone.)
6. Cook the pho rice noodles according to the package by placing the noodles in a pot of boiling water for 6-8 minutes until cooked. Then drain and rinse in cold water.
7. Wash all your herbs and garnishes and set them aside on a platter.
8. Once the Instant Pot is done cooking, unplug it and let it rest for 45 minutes. Release the steam after 45 minutes of resting.
9. Bring a pot of water to a boil and flash cook your meats (thinly sliced ribeye beef, the eye of round, tripe, and meatballs) for 2-5 minutes.
10. Drain and rinse the meats. Set aside on a platter.
11. Assemble your pho bowl with noodles, meats, and garnishes.
12. Ladle hot pho broth into your bowl and squeeze a wedge of lime juice on top.
13. Add your desired condiments.

Spicy Red Curry Shrimp

Ingredients:

2 tablespoons butter
6 cloves garlic (minced)
3 tablespoons ginger (minced)
3 tablespoons red or yellow curry paste
2 teaspoons fish sauce
1 cup chicken broth
3 tablespoons sugar
1 can coconut cream
½ can tomato sauce
2 pounds pre-cooked shrimp
2 red, orange, or yellow bell peppers (chopped)
1 cup green onions (chopped)

Optional:
fresh chili peppers or dried chili flakes

Sides:
sourdough bread, French baguette, or rice

Directions:
1. In a saucepan, on medium-high heat, melt the butter.
2. Add minced garlic and ginger. Stir-fry for two minutes.
3. Add curry paste and fish sauce. Mix well.
4. Add chicken broth and sugar. Mix until the sugar dissolves evenly.
5. Pour in a whole can of coconut cream and half a can of tomato sauce. Don't be shy!
6. Taste the sauce and add a splash of fish sauce or teaspoon of sugar according to your taste.
7. If you'd like the sauce to be spicier, add the chili peppers or flakes.
8. Add the bell peppers and simmer for five minutes.
9. Add the shrimp and simmer for another five to ten minutes.
10. Stir in half of the green onions and reserve the other half to garnish.
11. Dip your bread in the curry or enjoy the curry over rice.

Thịt Kho Tàu (Caramelized Pork & Eggs)

Ingredients:

2 pounds boneless country-style pork shoulder or pork belly (cubed into 1-inch pieces)
*You can do half shoulder and half pork belly
6 hard-boiled eggs (shell peeled)
2 tablespoons caramel cooking sauce or sweet soy sauce
½ cup fish sauce
12 fluid ounce can of coconut soda
2 teaspoons salt
2 teaspoons sugar
1 teaspoon ground black pepper

Garnish:
green onions (chopped)

Side:
jasmine rice (cooked)
pickled veggies (e.g. mustard greens)

Directions:
1. In a medium-size pot, bring 8 cups of water to a boil on high heat.
2. Add the eggs and boil for five minutes.
3. At the five minute mark, add the cubed pork and let the pork and eggs boil together for another five minutes.
4. Drain and rinse the eggs and pork in cold water until both are cool to the touch.
5. Peel the eggshells and set the hard-boiled eggs aside.
6. In another pot, add 8 cups of water and bring to a boil.
7. Add the cooked pork to the pot and reduce the heat to medium.
8. Add fish sauce, coconut soda, salt, sugar, and caramel cooking sauce.
9. Stir and reduce heat to a low. Taste the broth and add more salt or sugar according to your preference.
10. Simmer on low, uncovered, for twenty minutes.
11. Add the hard-boiled eggs and simmer for another 20 minutes.
12. Taste the broth again and add more sugar or salt according to taste.
13. Simmer for 10 more minutes, then turn off the heat. The pork should be very tender.
14. Pour the caramelized pork and eggs into a large serving bowl, sprinkle black pepper on top, and garnish with green onions.
15. Serve with rice and pickled veggies.

Volcano Pizzas (Hawaiian & Italian)

These pizzas are called volcanos because they are spicy. You can adjust the spice level by moderating the amount of black pepper and chili paste in your sauce, as well as jalapenos on your pizza.

Crust:
3 1/3 cups flour plus ¼ cup for dusting
½ tablespoon salt
1 tablespoon honey
1 ¼ cup warm water, 100-110 degrees Fahrenheit
½ teaspoon active dry yeast
2 tablespoons olive oil

Directions for the crust:
1. In a small bowl, stir together water and honey.
2. Add yeast to the honey water and let it sit for five minutes, then stir together.
3. In a separate large bowl, combine flour and salt.
4. Slowly add the water mixture and fold in with a spatula.
5. Knead the dough with your hands for a few minutes. The dough will be sticky and so will your hands.
6. Cover the bowl with a plastic wrap and let it sit at room temperature for 5 hours. The dough will double in size.
7. While you're waiting for the dough to rise, prepare the pizza sauce and toppings.
8. When you are ready to roll the dough, preheat the oven to 400 degrees Fahrenheit.
9. Dust the countertop with flour and knead the dough, folding it 8-10 times.
10. Divide the dough in half to make two pizzas.
11. Use some of the flour to dust the rolling pin and roll each dough ball into a round crust about 12-14 inches.
12. Brush each crust with a tablespoon of oil.
13. Line two pizza pans with parchment paper and place the crusts on each pan.
14. Bake at 400 degrees for 8 minutes, then remove from the oven.

Sauce:
*This recipe will yield extra sauce for dipping if you serve pizza with breadsticks or freeze the sauce to make other pasta dishes such as spaghetti, lasagne, ravioli, or tortellini.

4-14.5 ounce cans fire-roasted tomatoes
4 cloves garlic (minced)
2 tablespoons Italian seasoning
1 teaspoon salt
1 tablespoon ground black pepper (be generous if you like it spicy)
1 cup basil (chopped)
Optional: 1 tablespoon flour or corn starch for a thicker sauce.

Directions for the pizza sauce:
1. Put all the ingredients *except the basil and flour/corn starch* into a blender and pulse on low for 30 seconds to a minute.
2. Taste the sauce and add more salt or black pepper according to your taste.
3. Pour the sauce into a saucepan and bring to a low boil on medium-high heat.
4. Reduce the heat and stir in flour or corn starch if you'd like a thicker sauce.
5. Simmer on low heat with the cover on for 10 minutes.
6. Turn off the stove and remove the pan from the heat.
7. Let the sauce sit for 5-10 minutes to thicken and cool.
8. Gently fold in the chopped basil.

Toppings:
For the Hawaiian pizza:
- slices of cooked ham
- pineapple chunks or slices, fresh or canned (drained)
- jalapeno peppers, thinly sliced
- mozzarella and parmesan cheese (shredded/grated)

For the Italian pizza:
- slices of peppered salami
- sliced pepperoncini peppers
- red onion (diced)
- grape tomatoes (halved lengthwise)
- jalapeno peppers, thinly sliced
- mozzarella and parmesan cheese (shredded/grated)

Assembly:
1. Preheat the oven to 400 degrees Fahrenheit.
2. Spread enough pizza sauce on each crust to cover the whole pizza.

3. Sprinkle a generous amount of mozzarella and parmesan cheese on top of the sauce and cover the whole pie.
4. Add the toppings. I usually start with the meats then finish with the fruits and veggies.
5. Bake for 10 minutes and remove the pizzas. Enjoy right away.

SWEET TREATS

"We hide Amy's food from the kids when she cooks for us.
Sorry. Not sorry."
—**Tricia and Blake Rutledge, Foodies**

Cà Phê Sữa (Vietnamese Coffee)

Ingredients:

3 tablespoons chicory ground coffee
(I prefer Café Du Monde or Trung Nguyen Premium Coffee)
1-3 tablespoons condensed milk (sweetness according to taste)
1-2 tablespoons creamer (optional if you want your coffee extra creamy)
6-8 ounces of hot water, around 194 degrees Fahrenheit, before boiling point.
1 cup crushed ice (optional if you want iced coffee)

Other:
6-ounce stainless steel coffee pot drip filter

Directions:
1. Spoon the condensed milk into an old-fashioned drinking glass.
2. Scoop 3 tablespoons of ground coffee into the stainless steel coffee pot drip filter. Do not pack the coffee down.
3. Assemble the filter gently in the stainless steel pot and turn it clockwise a couple of times. It should sit leveled and gently on the coffee grounds.
4. Place the coffee pot drip filter over the condensed milk, on top of the old-fashioned drinking glass.
5. Pour steaming hot water into the coffee pot drip filter and watch the coffee drip into the glass. It should drip nicely but not too fast.
6. If you do not like your coffee too strong, pour another 3-6 ounces of water into the coffee pot drip filter.
7. Once all the water has strained through the filter, remove the stainless steel coffee pot drip filter and place it on top of the stainless steel lid to catch excess liquids.
8. Mix the coffee and condensed milk with a spoon until evenly mixed.
9. Add more condensed milk if you like it sweeter.
10. Add creamer if you would like your coffee extra creamy.
11. If you prefer iced coffee, let your coffee cool down.
12. Fill a tall highball drinking glass with crushed ice.
13. Pour your French-Vietnamese coffee into the iced glass.

Chè Ba Màu (Three Color Dessert)

Ingredients:

Red layer:
1 can sweet red kidney beans (drained)

Yellow layer:
½ cup dried mung beans
3-4 tablespoons sugar
4 cups water

Green layer:
1 tablespoon agar agar powder
2 cups water
¼ teaspoon pandan extract or green food coloring
3 tablespoons sugar

Coconut cream:
1 can coconut milk
3 tablespoons sugar
1 teaspoon tapioca starch or cornstarch

Other:
3 cups shaved ice

Directions:
1. Soak the yellow mung beans in water for 4-5 hours or overnight, then drain the water.
2. In a pot over medium-high heat, cook the mung beans in four cups of water until the beans are soft. Stir frequently so the beans do not stick together or burn. Add more water as needed.
   **If you have a rice cooker, cook the mung beans in the rice cooker instead with ¾ cup of water on the regular rice setting.
3. Once the mung bean is cooked, mash the beans into a paste. Mix in 3 tablespoons of sugar and taste. Add another tablespoon of sugar if you prefer a sweeter mung bean paste. Set aside in the fridge to chill.
4. In a saucepan, bring 2 cups of water to a boil and stir in the agar agar powder until it dissolves.
5. Add the pandan extract or food coloring and turn off the heat. Stir the mixture evenly then pour into a glass container.
6. Let the pandan jelly cool down before chilling it in the fridge for 2-3 hours.

7. Once the jelly is thickened cut the pandan jelly into strips.
8. In a saucepan, whisk together the coconut milk, 3 tablespoons of sugar, and tapioca starch or cornstarch.
9. Heat the coconut cream on medium heat for 3+ minutes until it thickens. Remove from heat and let it cool down before putting it in the fridge to chill for an hour.
10. To assemble, put a layer of shaved ice on the bottom, then sweet red kidney beans, a thin layer of shaved ice, then mung beans, then pandan jelly. Top the dessert with more shaved ice and pour the sweet coconut cream on top.
11. Shovel the dessert in your mouth with a spoon and enjoy the chilled three-color dessert. It tastes better if you are in a hammock with a tropical breeze and a view of the beach!

Chè Thái (Thai Fruit Cocktail)

Ingredients:

Gelatin:
1 package coconut gelatin mix
1 package almond gelatin mix
½ package agar-agar powder (cook with 2 cups of water)
½ cup sugar

Directions for the gelatins:
1. Prepare the coconut gelatin and almond gelatin mixes according to the instructions on the package.
2. For the agar-agar, in a small pot with 2 cups of water, whisk in the agar-agar powder and sugar.
3. Bring it to a boil for 2 minutes then pour it into a glass container. Let it cool down before chilling it in the fridge for 2 hours.
4. Cut the agar-agar jelly, almond gelatin, & coconut gelatin into cubes.
5. Chill the gelatin mix in the fridge.

Imitation Pomegranate:
1 can water chestnuts, cut into small pieces
1 cup tapioca flour or cornstarch
2 drops red food color

Directions for the imitation pomegranate:
1. Put the chopped water chestnuts in a bowl and mix in 2 drops of red food coloring.
2. Add the red chestnuts to a ziplock bag. Pour in the tapioca flour and seal the bag. Shake it until all the chestnuts are coated in flour.
3. Pour the floured chestnuts into a colander and sift out the excess flour.
4. Prepare a bowl of cold water. You will be transferring your cooked chestnuts into a cold bath.
5. Bring a pot of water to a boil and then add the red, floured chestnuts. Let it boil for two minutes. When it floats to the top, it is ready.
6. Using a slotted ladle, transfer the chestnuts to your cold bath and let them soak in the cold water. Drain the water once the chestnuts are cool.
7. Chill the imitation pomegranate in the fridge.

Cream:
1 quart of half and half

1/3 cup condensed milk

Directions for the cream:
1. Mix the half and half with the condensed milk until smooth.
2. Chill in the fridge until ready for assembly.

Fruits:
2 cans longan with juice
1 can coconut meat (drained, cut into strips)
1 can coconut jelly and papaya (drained)
1 can jackfruit (drained, cut into strips)
1 can toddy palm seeds (drained, rinsed)

Directions for the fruits:
1. In a large bowl, combine all the canned fruits, making sure to drain all of the liquids except the longan. Keep the longan juice.
2. Cut the coconut meat and jackfruit into strips.
3. Chill the fruit bowl in the fridge until you're ready to assemble.

Assembling the fruit cocktail:
1. Remove the fruit bowl out of the fridge and pour in the gelatins, the imitation pomegranates, and the cream.
2. Ladle the fruit cocktail into a tall glass and enjoy. Feel free to add shaved ice to the glass but the cocktail should already be chilled.
3. Now, put on your sunglasses, regardless of the weather, because when you're this cool, the sun always shines.

Coconut Rum Banana Bread

Ingredients:

Bread:
2 cups flour
¾ teaspoon baking soda
½ teaspoon salt
1 cup granulated sugar
¼ cup butter, softened
2 eggs
5 very ripe bananas
¼ cup plain yogurt
1/3 cup of coconut rum
½ teaspoon vanilla extract
1 cup sweetened coconut flakes or shredded coconut

Glaze:
2 cups sweetened coconut flakes or shredded coconut
1 cup powdered sugar
1 tablespoon of fresh lemon juice or lemon curd
¼ cup coconut rum

Directions:
1. Preheat oven to 350 degrees Fahrenheit.
2. Combine the flour, baking soda, and salt in a bowl.
3. In a separate large bowl, combine the butter and sugar. Beat with a hand mixer until well-blended.
4. Add the eggs and continue beating until mixed well.
5. Add in the yogurt, bananas, rum, and vanilla extract.
6. Beat until blended, then add in the flour mixture. Beat on low until mixed. Stir in 1 cup of the coconut flakes.
7. Spoon the batter into a 9x5 inch loaf pan coated with cooking oil.
8. Bake for one hour. Meanwhile, prepare the glaze.
9. In a bowl, combine powdered sugar, lemon juice or curd, coconut flakes, and coconut rum. Mix well and taste. If your tummy feels warm from the rum, it's okay. This is adulting. Want it sweeter? No problem, add more powdered sugar!
10. Once the bread is cooked, transfer it to a cooling rack for ten minutes.
11. Lather, don't drizzle, the tops of the warm banana bread with the coconut rum glaze.
12. Make it a party with some long island iced tea!

Cream Puffs

Ingredients:

Powdered sugar for dusting

Puff pastry:
1 cup water
½ cup butter, softened
1 cup flour
4 eggs

Directions for the puff pastries:
1. Preheat the oven to 400 degrees Fahrenheit.
2. Mix the water and butter and heat it in a saucepan on medium heat.
3. Lower the heat and stir in the flour vigorously until it forms a ball.
4. Beat in the eggs, one at a time, thoroughly.
5. Use a cookie scooper and drop a scoop of dough onto an ungreased baking sheet, three inches apart.
6. Bake for 40-45 minutes and let the puffs cool on a cooling rack.

Cream filling:
2 cups whole milk
1 teaspoon vanilla extract
1 cup sugar
½ cup flour
½ teaspoon salt
2 eggs, yolks separated
½ teaspoon lemon zest

Directions for the cream filling:
1. Bring the milk to a boil in a saucepan, then add the vanilla extract. Remove from heat but keep the stove on.
2. In a bowl, mix the egg yolks with only half of the sugar (i.e. ½ cup) and ½ teaspoon of salt.
3. Add half of the warm milk into the sugar and eggs bowl. Mix well.
4. Add the lemon zest, then pour the mixture into the warm milk in the saucepan.
5. Bring it to a boil while stirring until the filling thickens.
6. Remove the filling from the heat and pour it into a bowl or pan. Let it cool in a bed of ice.

7. While the filling cools, use a hand mixer to whip together on medium-high speed the egg whites and remaining ½ cup of sugar until a meringue with stiff peak forms.
8. Combine both mixtures of the beaten egg whites with the cooled cream filling.

Assembling the cream puffs:
1. Poke a small hole at the bottom of each puff pastry.
2. Pour the cream filling into a piping bag and fill each puff pastry with the custard.
3. Dust the tops of each cream puff.
4. Chill the pastries for an hour in the fridge before eating, if you can be patient!
5. I bet you can't eat just one!

Da Ua (Vietnamese Yogurt)

Ingredients:

1-14 ounce can sweetened condensed milk
1 ¼ cup boiling water
2 ½ cups whole milk (1% or 2% is fine)
1 ¼ cup plain yogurt (I prefer Greek yogurt)
Yogurt must contain active cultures
1 cup water

Other:
large Instant Pot preferred but not required.
7 – 8 ounce glass jars with lids (If no lid, use aluminum foil)
Any size and type of glass jars will do, such as mason jars or baby food jars.

Directions:
1. In a large bowl, whisk together condensed milk and boiled water until the condensed milk dissolves and well-mixed together.
2. Add cold milk straight from the refrigerator and mix well. The higher the milk fat, the creamier the yogurt. Adding cold milk ensures the mixture is below 130 degrees Fahrenheit. Active cultures will die if the temperature is above 130 degrees.
3. Add plain yogurt to the mixing bowl and whisk until smooth.
4. Pour the mixture into the glass jars and cover with a lid or aluminum foil.
5. Prepare the Instant Pot by adding one cup of water and placing the steaming trivet into the pot.
**If you do not have an instant pot, place all the jars in the oven. Keep the oven off but the oven light on and incubate for 11 hours.
6. Place all the jars into the Instant Pot. It is alright to stack the jars.
7. Close the lid, ensure the vent is sealed, and select the "Yogurt" option on the Instant Pot.
8. Set the time to 11 hours and start the incubation. "Yogt" will display on the Instant Pot once the incubation is done.
9. Remove the jars and refrigerate for a couple of hours. The yogurt will keep for two weeks in the refrigerator – longer if you transfer to the freezer after two hours of refrigeration.
**Enjoy frozen yogurt for a nice treat on a hot day.
10. Optional: Top yogurt with fruits or granola.

Dalgona (Whipped Coffee)

Ingredients:
4 tablespoons instant coffee
4 tablespoons sugar
4 tablespoons hot water
milk (your choice – 2%, almond, soy, coconut, whole, oat, etc)
ice cubes
Optional: Baileys Irish Cream or Grind coffee liqueur
Optional garnish: espresso beans

Directions:
1. Whisk together the instant coffee, sugar, and hot water until it thickens and peaks form. I start with a hand whisk then move to an electric hand mixer.
2. Don't give up. It will take some time to thicken and form majestic, caramel-colored peaks.
3. Fill a glass with ice. Add a teaspoon or an ounce of Baileys Irish Cream or Grind coffee liquor. It depends on how much of a good time we're having. Skip the Baileys or Grind if we're being good.
4. Add milk to the glass, leaving a half-inch available for the whipped coffee.
5. Spoon as much whipped coffee as you want on top and garnish with espresso beans if you're "bougie boozy."
6. Drink the dalgona with a straw or gently mix the whipped coffee into your milk and enjoy.

Flan/Purin (Caramel Pudding)

Ingredients:

Flan:
6 eggs
2 teaspoons vanilla extract
3 cups half and half
1 cup sugar

Directions for the flan:
1. Beat the eggs and vanilla together well then set aside.
2. Heat the sugar and half and half on medium heat until the sugar is melted and the color is caramel brown.
3. Pour the sweet milk into the eggs and vanilla mixture.
4. Strain the mixture so the batter is smooth and creamy.

Caramel:
1 cup sugar
4 tablespoons water

Directions for the caramel sauce:
1. Heat the sugar and water on the stove in a small pan until the sugar is melted and the color is a caramel brown color.
2. Evenly distribute the caramel into the ramekins or small tart pans. The caramel will harden quickly.

Other:
8 ramekins or 4 small pie tart pans
10"x14" baking pan
aluminum foil
strainer

Directions:
1. Preheat the oven to 300 degrees Fahrenheit.
2. Fill the baking pan with hot water to the level that is half the height of the ramekins or tart pans.
3. Place the pan of water in the oven while the oven is preheating.
4. Prepare the flan as directed above then make the caramel as noted above.
5. Pour the flan batter into the caramel-coated ramekins or tart pans.
6. Cover each with aluminum foil.

7. Place the ramekins or tart pans <u>carefully</u> into the hot water in the pan and bake for 40 minutes.
8. Remove the flans from the oven and let them cool for 30 minutes before putting them in the fridge to cool and set for about 3 hours.
9. To serve, put the ramekins or tart pans in a pan of very hot water. Let it sit for a few minutes to warm up the caramel.
10. Loosen the edges/sides of the flan with a butter knife or silicone spatula before flipping it over onto a flat plate.
11. Ring a bell. Your taste testers will come running.

Lemon Cheesecake

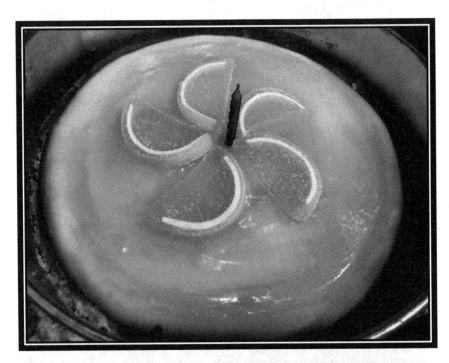

Ingredients:

Crust:
2 cups honey graham cracker crumbs
1/3 cup melted butter

Directions for the crust:
1. Crush the graham crackers into fine crumbles using a pestle and mortar.
2. Pour in the melted butter and combine evenly.

Filling:
4-8 ounce packages of cream cheese, softened
1 ½ cups sugar
4 tablespoons flour
1 teaspoons vanilla extract
1 teaspoon lemon extract
4 eggs (beaten)

Directions for the filling:
1. Using a hand mixer, mix the softened cream cheese and sugar evenly, then add the flour and continue mixing.
2. Add in the vanilla and eggs. Mix well to remove the lumps.

Lemon curd frosting:
4 lemons, zested and juiced
1 ½ cups sugar
1 stick of butter, softened
4 eggs
1 jar Dickinson's lemon curd or Trader Joe's lemon curd

Directions for the lemon curd:
1. Combine the lemon zest and sugar in a food processor. Pulse it until the combination is finely minced.
2. In a medium-sized bowl, cream together the butter and lemon zest.
3. Beat in the eggs, then add the lemon juice. Mix well.
4. Pour the lemon mixture into a saucepan and cook on medium heat until it thickens, stirring frequently.
5. Let the lemon curd cool, then add the store-bought jar of lemon curd to the homemade lemon curd. Mix evenly.
6. Cover it and put it in the fridge to chill for an hour.

Other:

food processor
pestle and mortar
cooking spray
springform pan
aluminum foil
spatula
large pie dish filled with water
electric hand mixer

Directions:

1. Preheat the oven to 350 degrees Fahrenheit.
2. Place a pie dish filled with water on the bottom rack and let the water heat up in the oven.
3. Line the bottom of the springform pan with aluminum foil.
4. Grease the bottom and sides of the pan with cooking oil.
5. Pour the graham cracker crumbles into the springform pan and press the crust out evenly and firmly.
6. Pour in the cheesecake filling (the batter) on top of the crust.
7. Place the springform pan on the rack directly above the hot water in the oven.
8. Bake for one hour then remove the springform pan out of the oven.
9. Drape a kitchen towel over the pan. Let it cool for 2 hours before putting it in the fridge to chill overnight. (Keep it in the pan.)
10. Prepare the lemon curd frosting per the directions above.
11. Remove the cheesecake from the springform pan and frost the top of the cheesecake with the lemon curd.

Mango Sticky Rice

Ingredients:

1.5 cups glutinous rice
19 fl. oz. can coconut cream
1/3 cup sugar
2 tablespoons sesame seeds (lightly toasted)
6 champagne or honey mangos

Directions:
1. Wash and rinse the rice a few times until the water runs clear.
2. Drain the rice into a sieve and steam the rice over a pot of boiling water with the lid on for 60-90 minutes. You can also cook it in a rice cooker like regular white rice. The rice should be sticky and moist.
3. In a small saucepan on high heat, bring the coconut cream to a boil.
4. Add the sugar to the coconut cream and stir until dissolved.
5. Remove the coconut cream from the heat and spoon 1 cup of it into a small bowl. Put the small bowl in the fridge to chill for 30 minutes.
6. Peel and cut up the mangos into cubes.
7. Once the rice is cooked, transfer it to a bowl and pour the coconut cream over the rice.
8. Mix the rice and coconut cream and let the rice soak in the cream for 30 minutes.
9. To serve, scoop the sticky rice into a serving bowl or plate, drizzle the chilled coconut cream on top, sprinkle some toasted sesame seeds on top, and spoon the cut mangos over the sticky rice.

Raspberry Lemon Cake

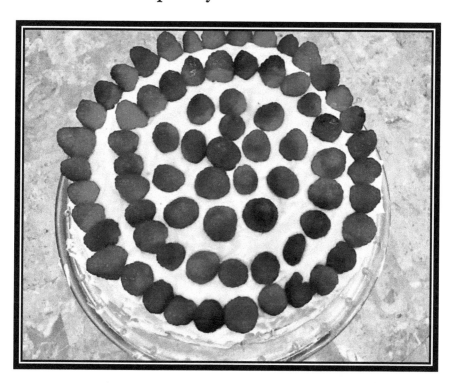

Ingredients:

Cake batter:
1 stick unsalted butter, softened
1 stick salted butter, softened
1 ½ cups sugar
¼ cup brown sugar
1 teaspoon lemon extract
1 teaspoon vanilla extract
1 lemon, zested and juiced
4 eggs
2 ½ cup cake flour
1 ½ teaspoon baking powder
½ teaspoon baking soda
½ cup milk (2% or whole)
½ cup sour cream
1 cup of raspberries

Directions for the batter:
1. In a large bowl, using an electric hand mixer on medium speed, combine the butter, sugars, extracts, and lemon zest and juice.
2. Add the eggs, one at a time, and continue mixing. Set aside.
3. In a separate bowl, whisk the cake flour, baking powder, and baking soda.
4. Add the dry mixture to the wet mixture and mix on low speed for a minute. It will be lumpy.
5. Add in the milk and sour cream. Use a spatula to fold the batter gently together and mix evenly but do not over mix otherwise your cake will be dry and dense. We want them fluffy and moist!
6. Fold in the fresh raspberries.

Filling:
1 jar of homemade or store-bought lemon curd

Frosting:
8 ounces cream cheese, softened
1 stick of salted butter, softened
3 cups powdered sugar
1 tablespoon lemon zest
1 tablespoon lemon juice
½ teaspoon lemon extract

3 tablespoons sour cream

Directions for the frosting:
1. In a large bowl, using an electric hand mixer on low speed beat the cream cheese and butter until it is fluffy.
2. Add in the powdered sugar and continue mixing on low speed.
3. Add the lemon zest, lemon juice, and lemon extract and mix until creamy.
4. Add the sour cream and increase the speed to medium. Continue mixing until the frosting is light and creamy.

Garnish:
3 cups fresh raspberries

Other:
cooking oil
2-9 inch cake pans
parchment paper, cut into two 9-inch circles for each cake pan
electric hand mixer
whisk
spatula
cooling racks

Directions:
1. Preheat the oven to 350 degrees Fahrenheit.
2. Coat the sides and bottoms of each cake pan with oil.
3. Place the parchment paper circles on the bottoms of each cake pan and coat the parchment paper with oil.
4. Pour the cake batter evenly into each cake pan and bake for 40 minutes. The tops should be firm and golden.
5. Test the cakes by inserting a toothpick or fork into them. If it pulls out dry, your cakes are done.
6. Let the cakes cool in the pan for ten minutes, then remove the cakes and allow them to cool completely on cooling racks.
7. Place one of the cakes on a plate or cake stand and spread a thin layer of lemon curd on top. Use the whole jar.
8. Spread the frosting all around the sides of the cake.
9. Gently place the second cake on top of the first one and press firmly down to seal the two cakes together with the layer of lemon curd.
10. Put the cake in the fridge to set for 20 minutes then resume frosting the rest of the cake, sides, and top.

11. Put the cake back in the fridge to chill for 20 minutes.
12. Now you are ready to decorate the cake with fresh strawberries.

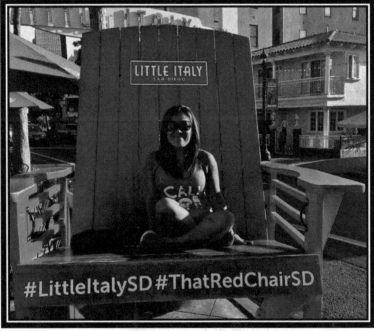

"Get in my belly!"
—**Jennifer Hwang, Escrow Officer**

Joe Walls, my "will work for food" photographer

Amy supervising Joe, supervising Preston

Chloe, our quiet kitchen stalker, waiting for a treat

Ike, our kitchen cleaning crew

Follow Amy on social media!
#SnowinVietnam
#SnowinSeattle
#SnowsKitchen

https://www.facebook.com/authoramymle
https://www.facebook.com/quillhawkpublishing/
https://twitter.com/amy_m_le
https://twitter.com/hawk_quill
https://www.linkedin.com/in/amymle/
https://www.etsy.com/shop/QuillHawkPublishing
https://www.instagram.com/amy_m_le/
https://www.instagram.com/quillhawkpublishing/
http://www.amy-m-le.com

About the Author

Amy M. Le was born in Vietnam and immigrated to The United States in 1980 at the age of five with her mother and cousin. She graduated from Western Washington University with a degree in Sociology and worked in the telecommunications and technology sectors for twenty years. Amy calls the Pacific Northwest and Oklahoma her home. Her greatest joys are spending time with her family, cooking, and traveling.

CPSIA information can be obtained
at www.ICGtesting.com
Printed in the USA
LVHW081143110421
684149LV00003B/44